ENTOMOLOGY

Living with Insects

Jonathan Neal

Purdue University

Kendall Hunt
publishing company

Cover and interior images provided by Jonathan Neal.

www.kendallhunt.com
Send all inquiries to:
4050 Westmark Drive
Dubuque, IA 52004-1840

Printed in the United States of America
10   9   8   7   6   5   4   3

Contents

Introduction

Insect Numbers and Diversity

It is impossible to live on the planet earth and not encounter insects. Insects are the largest group of animals in terms of numbers of individuals, total biomass, and numbers of species. The numbers of insect individuals alive at any one time are vast. A single group of insects, the ants, has at any one time more living individuals than any other group of land animals. Many people are surprised to learn that the biomass of ants is four times greater than biomass of land vertebrates. Although an individual ant weighs several orders of magnitude less than a large mammal like an elephant, the massive numbers of ants tip the scales.

Well over half of all described species of multi-cellular organisms are insects (around 925,000 insect species worldwide). Those are just the species that have been described. It is estimated that more species of insects are unknown to man than have been described. By comparison, only about 3 percent of described species are chordates, the group that includes, fish, reptiles, birds, and mammals (see Figure 1).

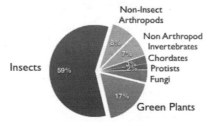

Composition of Described Species

Insects 59%

Non-Insect Arthropods 8%

Non Arthropod Invertebrates 7%

Chordates 3%

Protists 2%

Fungi

Green Plants 17%

Most people are familiar with only a few types of insects they routinely encounter. Entomologists, are familiar with more of the insect species than most people, but as Oliver Wendell Holmes wrote,

> *"No man can be truly called an entomologist, sir; the subject is too vast for any single human intelligence to grasp."*[1]

Because of the vastness of the subject, most entomologists specialize and focus on one or a few types of insects. Still, the numbers of insect species are far greater than the number of entomologists who study them. Many species of insects exist in obscurity and may forever escape notice from humans. The amazing feats and life histories of countless species of insects will go untold.

Why Study Insects?

Insects have a large impact on our environment and are incorporated into our cultures in many ways. Even if we are not looking for insects, many insects will find us, including mosquitoes that stop by for a quick blood meal or ants and wasps that visit food at our picnics. Insects affect our lives with no respect for our personal preferences.

Insects evoke strong reactions in many people. Most people will be stung during their lifetime by a wasp. This can provoke fear. Many people associate insects with filth. That can provoke disgust. We often resort to emotional reactions when we possess too little understanding and knowledge. Learning about wasps can make their behavior less unpredictable to us. This can turn fear into a healthy respect. Learning about the important roles that insects have in our ecosystem can turn disgust and contempt into appreciation. Learning more about insects is critical to efforts to address important insect vectored diseases such as malaria. Learning more about insects allows us to take actions that accentuate the positive effects of insects, diminish the negative impact of pest insects and come to an accommodation with this important group of animals that share our world.

Science can present us with information about insects from the point of view of the objective observer. However, the interactions between humans and insects are more fully explored by the arts. Insect sounds can influence music, provide rhythms, and be the subject of lyrics. Many musicians are attuned to the sounds of their environment. These sounds include the calls of cicadas, crickets, katydids, and the buzz of the bumblebee. Some artists incorporate insect sounds as part of their recorded music performance.

Insects are popular subjects of artists and appear in all art forms. Insects such as butterflies can communicate beauty and freedom. Wasps communicate strength and threat. Ants communicate hard work and perseverance. Insects stimulate curiosity of young children and are often the subject of children's books and songs. Film makers take advantage of fear of insects to make horror films starring giant insects or genetically engineered swarms that wreak havoc on society. From art and music, we learn to more fully appreciate our complex relationships to insects.

This book is not meant to be a comprehensive treatment of the study of insects. Rather, it is intended to highlight some of the interesting and fascinating features of insects for those who possess only a casual familiarity with the study of insects.

Chapter 1

The Origins of the Arthropods and Insects

Key Concepts in Biology

All Life Is Related

The modern understanding of biological organisms and biodiversity is based on a few key concepts. At the root of our understanding is the concept, "All life is related." This concept is based on evidence from multiple sources that all modern living organisms are descendants of a single ancestral life form that existed billions of years ago.

The concept that all life is related is important in biology because it provides a basis for making useful predictions. If two living organisms are related, then core processes are likely to be similar. "All organisms are related" means that information gained from the study of insects may be applicable to other living organisms, including humans. For example, the fruit fly, *Drosophila*, has been used as a model system to investigate genetics and inheritance. Much of what we learn from the study of Drosophila is directly applicable to humans. Some genes of *Drosophila* are similar to genes in humans and all living organisms because all life is related. If all living organisms were not related, we would have little basis to assume that a process would be similar in different organisms.

Descent With Modification

All life is related through a common ancestor. The descendants of that ancestor display the wide diversity of life on earth that we observe today. A key characteristic of living organisms is self-replication—parents produce offspring. Offspring are similar to the parents, but not exact replicas. Thus, the replication process can be described as "descent with modification." Over many generations, the accumulated modifications can result in descendents that are markedly different from the ancestor. For example, we know that all domesticated dogs are descendents of wolves, but a poodle and a greyhound have markedly different characteristics from a wolf and from each other. Similarly, we know that all beetles share a common ancestor and several characteristics are common to the entire group, but beetles differ markedly in their appearance. For example, a firefly is easily distinguished from a dung beetle even though both are clearly beetles.

Natural Selection

The enormous biodiversity of species present today was produced by a combination of descent with modification and natural selection. Descent with modification produces variation within populations for inherited traits. However, individuals must function in an environment and some function better than others. Natural selection describes the observation that some individuals successfully reproduce while others die without reproducing. Successful reproduction depends on the interaction of inherited traits an individual possesses and the environmental conditions. Inherited traits that favor reproduction will increase in frequency the next generation because the successful parents (who by definition possess successful traits) will pass those traits to their offspring. Inherited traits that reduce or eliminate reproduction will decrease in frequency the next generation because parents that carry less successful traits will contribute fewer offspring to the next generation or in some cases, none at all and those genetic traits meet an evolutionary dead end. As a result of natural selection, individuals appear to be adapted to their environment because those individuals that are not adapted to their environment do not reproduce (by definition) and those genetic traits go extinct.

Speciation

Whether or not a trait increases or decreases reproduction depends on the environment. Numerous factors can reduce or eliminate reproduction and may include lack of necessary resources, inability to compete for resources, susceptibility to diseases, susceptibility to predation, or inability to withstand abiotic factors such as temperature or moisture. A trait that enhances reproduction under one set of environmental conditions may reduce or eliminate reproduction in a different environment. If an insect population spreads into two dissimilar environments (A and B), the traits adapted to environment A will increase in the populations in environment A and the traits adapted to environment B will increase in the populations in environment B. Over many generations, the populations will diverge in their characteristics as each population becomes better adapted to its local environment. Eventually, these differences can accumulate so that the two populations become distinct species.

For example, a leaf insect species may be capable of eating a plant with red leaves and another plant with green leaves. However, birds (that use keen vision to see insect prey) will eliminate red insects that are easily found on the green plants and the green insects that are easily found on the red plants. Those insects that survive on the green plants will be those that blend in the best with the green plants and those that survive on the red plants will be those that blend in best with the red plants (because of predation). Those insects that survive predation will pass on their traits to the next generation.

Many generations of descent with modification and natural selection will eliminate combinations of traits that make the insects visible to predators leaving only those combinations of traits that best disguise the insects from predators. This can include mechanisms that prevent red insects from mating with green ones and producing hybrid offspring that do not survive on either red or green plants. Descent with modification combined with natural selection could produce two different (but related) insect species—a green species that prefers living on the green plants and a red species that prefers red plants.

Because there are so many species of insects, we find many examples among insects of populations that are in various stage of speciation. Our common Eastern Black Swallowtail butterfly, *Papilo polyxenes,* is closely related to the Anise Swallowtail, *Papilio zelicaon,* that is found on the Pacific coast of North America. The two populations are separated by mountains and are considered distinct species. However, in areas of the western United States where the populations overlap, some interbreeding can occur. In the interbreeding area, hybrid "nitra" swallowtails are produced. The hybrids cannot produce fertile offspring when mating with the Eastern Black Swallowtail, but can produce a few offspring when mating with Anise Swallowtails. This is one of many examples of speciation that is still in process and not yet complete.

Habitats, Microhabitats, and Species Diversity

Within an area, there will be a much larger diversity of insect species than species of larger animals. Due to their smaller size, more distinct habitats are available to insects. For example, a large grazing animal such as a bison needs a pasture with millions of individual plants in order to grow and reproduce. Because of its large size, the bison experiences the entire pasture as a single habitat. A small insect may complete its entire development in the seed of a single plant or on the leaves or roots of a single plant. The pasture may contain many species of plants, each plant a separate "microhabitat" capable of supporting a different species of insect. Other insects may live on the bison or its manure. Because insects can divide a single "habit" into multiple "microhabitats," insects have orders of magnitude more unique habitats available than larger animals.

Nested Hierarchies

A consequence of descent with modification is that living organisms fall into a nested hierarchy pattern. A nested hierarchy has a root that forms branches; the branches themselves can form branches and so on. This pattern results when descendants many generations removed from an ancestral form become two or more separate groups that differ in key characteristics. For example, all arthropods share common characteristics of paired jointed appendages and an exoskeleton that contains chitin. Insects form a group that is "nested" within the arthropods. Insects share a common ancestor and a common set of characteristics that distinguish them from other arthropods. These characters include three body regions, and three pair of legs. Beetles are a group that is "nested" within the insects. All beetles share a common ancestor and have forewings that are modified into protective covers, a trait that distinguishes them from other groups of insects. Fireflies are a group that is nested within the beetles. All fireflies have a common ancestor and share important traits that distinguish them from other groups of beetles (Figure 1.1).

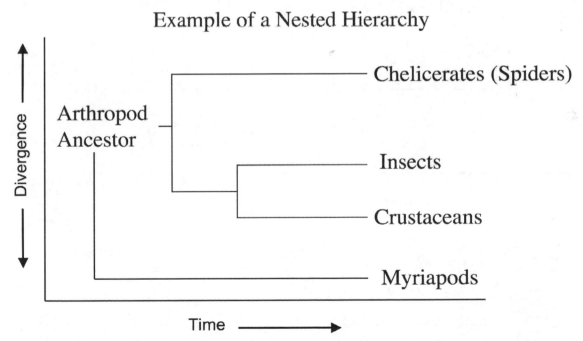

(Fig 1.1)   This abbreviated family tree for extant arthropod groups shows the patterns of descent with modification and the nested hierarchy structure.

Phylogeny

The nested hierarchy pattern reflects the phylogeny (or history of the lineages) of each species. Biologists work to reconstruct the phylogenies in the classification of species. Understanding how a species is related to similar organisms improves our ability to predict the presence or absence of many traits and to understand their biological function.

Milestones in the History of Insects and Other Life on Earth

The processes of descent with modification and natural selection have produced a remarkable diversity of living organisms. To understand insects and other living organisms it is useful to understand how they came to be and important events or "milestones" in evolution (Figure 1.2). Milestones include:

1. Self-replicating molecules.
2. The organized cell.
3. Photosynthesis.
4. Oxygenation of the atmosphere.
5. The Eukaryotic cell.
6. Multicellular organisms including arthropods.
7. First land plants.
8. The invasion of land by arthropods.
9. The first insects.
10. Flight and insects as the dominant species.

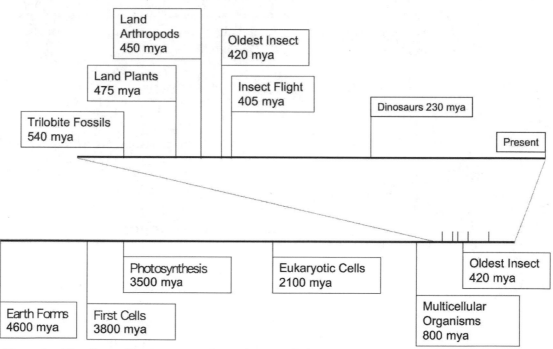

(Fig 1.2)   Timeline of key events in the evolution of life on earth.

1. The Age of the Earth and Self-Replicating Molecules

The earth is about 4600 million (4.6 billion) years old. The ancient earth contained oceans and continents, but no life. On this ancient lifeless earth, a wide variety of organic (carbon-containing) molecules were produced by natural processes. Among the diverse organic chemicals that are formed by natural processes, some have a very curious property—the ability to self-replicate (make copies of themselves). Self-replication, a core process of all living organisms, is inherent in some organic molecules. One type of self-replicating molecule, ribonucleic acid (RNA) is central to growth and reproduction of all extant living organisms. The conditions on the early earth would have allowed the production of self-replicating molecules and their replication including RNA.

Replication and Life on Earth

The exact nature of the first self-replicating molecules is unknown. Possible candidate molecules include RNA. Scientists have demonstrated in laboratories that simple RNA molecules can self-replicate without cells. In modern cells, RNA has a central role in the production of the molecules that form the building blocks of the cells. This role has led to much speculation that the path from self-replicating molecules to cellular organisms included RNA. Molecules that have the ability to self-replicate can increase greatly in number over time.

Molecules and Evolution

Self-replicating molecules exhibit properties that allow the action of evolution. "Parent" molecules produce "offspring" molecules (descent). Replication is not always exact. Most offspring molecules are identical to the parent molecules. Occasionally offspring molecules are produced that resemble the parent molecules but contain modifications. Thus, self-replicating molecules exhibit descent with modification.

How well a molecule with a modification will reproduce depends on the properties of the molecule and the effects of its environment. In other words, molecules are subject to "natural selection." Self-replicating molecules have a cycle of production and destruction. Those molecules with the best combination of rate of replication and stability persist and expand in numbers. Those molecules less capable of self-replication or more prone to destruction would become extinct. Thus, self-replicating molecules are subject to the same evolutionary processes—descent with modification and natural selection as cellular life.

2. The Evolution of Cells

The environment can be hostile to molecules and cause their rapid destruction. Some self-replicating molecules could have gained protection from the hostile environment by associating with other molecules. For example, some extant RNA viruses are protected from destruction by association with proteins (a protein coat). As an early step in the evolution of the cell, self-replicating molecules could have formed associations with other molecules and created a microenvironment that enhanced rates of reproduction and stability. The ability to make favorable modifications to its own microenvironment would further the success of a self-replicating molecule.

What Factors Favor the Evolution of Cells?

A cell features a membrane made of lipids that encloses the cell contents. The cell membrane (lipid) restricts movement of molecules in and out of the cells and affords protection for the cell components against the outside environment. The modern cell is an assemblage of self-replicating molecules (RNA and deoxyribonucleic acid [DNA]), structural molecules and enzymes (proteins produced by RNA), other molecules such as lipids and carbohydrates (produced by proteins), and inorganic molecules commonly found in nature.

Some organic chemicals are capable of self-assembly: They associate with other molecules to form more complex structures. In nature, lipids suspended in water can naturally form vesicles. Like cells, vesicles have an interior space that is completely surrounded by a bi-layer of lipid. Proteins are known for a remarkable ability to self-assemble into complex structures. These complex structures may include other proteins or other types of molecules such as lipids or nucleic acids. Self-replicating molecules that associated with the interiors of lipid vesicles would gain protection from the hostile environment. Cells may have evolved through opportunistic, stable associations of self-replicating molecules with the interiors of pre-existing vesicles.

The First cells

The first cells were probably crude, lacked many of the complex modifications present in modern cells, and probably could not compete with modern cells. However, being the first meant that there was little competition. As cells increased in number and competed for resources, natural selection favored the accumulation of more complex modifications. The process of accumulating more complex modifications led to the modern cell.

Eight hundred to one thousand million years passed from the formation of the earth to the first living cells. We know from fossils that the first cells appeared between 3.8 and 3.6 billion years ago. With the exception of viruses, all living organisms are composed of cells.

We do not know the exact length of time it took to go from crude associations of molecules to cells of the level of complexity and efficiency that are living today. The process could have spanned several hundred million years and billions of generations of descent with modification. However, once the modern cell evolved, it has persisted in a similar form for about 3.6 billion years.

The First Cells and Energy

The first cells probably depended upon oxidation-reduction reactions for their energy. The energy needed for this process is driven by the weathering of minerals or by hydrothermal vents. There are still single-cell organisms today that live near volcanic vents in the ocean floor and are dependent upon oxidation-reduction reactions for all their energy. However, the energy available to cells from these processes is limited compared to energy directly from the sun. Eventually a new process evolved that was capable of capturing energy directly from sunlight, photosynthesis.

3. Photosynthesis

Photosynthesis first occurred in blue-green algae around 3,500 million years ago (mya). Photosynthesis is a process of capturing energy directly from the sun, a much larger source of energy than oxidation-reduction reactions. Utilization of this new source of energy allowed the expansion of the number and diversity of cells and eventually led to important changes to the atmosphere of the earth. Sunlight contains energy in the form of photons. Photosynthetic cells have proteins that capture energy from the photons and use the energy to produce new cell components. In the process of capturing the energy in sunlight, photosynthetic organisms split molecules of water (H_2O) into hydrogen and oxygen. The hydrogen is used as the energy source for the cell. The free oxygen is released into the environment.

4. Photosynthesis and Atmospheric Alteration

The ancient earth atmosphere contained almost no oxygen. Most oxygen on the ancient earth was present in H_2O. Free oxygen, a product of photosynthesis, would quickly react with iron (iron oxide is "rust") and other elements. For over a 1,000 million years, oxygen produced by photosynthesis reacted with iron and other minerals in the water. The minerals in the water available for oxidation would not be depleted until about 2,100 mya. After the oxidation of minerals in the oceans was completed, the oxygen content in the water could increase.

As oxygen concentrations increased in the oceans, some oxygen would escape into the atmosphere where it would react with iron and other minerals on land. The oxidation of minerals on land would keep the concentration of oxygen in the atmosphere at very low levels for an additional 1,000 million years. Once the minerals available for oxidation were depleted, the concentration in the atmosphere slowly increased over a period of hundreds of millions more years. Eventually, atmospheric oxygen concentrations would reach about 20 percent, the concentration of oxygen present in our atmosphere today.

Until about 2,100 mya, all cells relied on anaerobic (absence of oxygen) processes to generate energy. Anaerobic processes are less efficient energy generators than aerobic processes. This limits the energy available to a cell and the size of the cell. The increase in oxygen concentrations in the oceans created an environment for the evolution of a new type of cell, the eukaryotic cell.

5. Eukaryotic Cells

Eukaryotic cells are capable of using oxygen in aerobic respiration for the production of energy. Eukaryotic cells are larger and more complex than the original prokaryotic cells. The eukaryotic cell was a necessary step in the evolution of multi-cellular organisms. Prokaryotic cells may form colonies, but over the past 3,800 million years, prokaryotic cells have never formed multicellular organisms. All extant multicellular plants and animals are made from eukaryotic cells.

The oldest fossils of eukaryotic cells are about 2,100 million years old. Eukaryotic cells as we know them could not have existed until after oxygen concentrations in the Earth's oceans had substantially increased. Eukaryotic cells use oxygen in reactions with sugars and lipids to provide the energy required for cell maintenance, growth and reproduction. Eukaryotic cells existed as single cells or in colonies of single-cell organisms for over 1,300 million years before the first multi-cellular eukaryotic organisms evolved.

6. Multi-Cellular Organisms

The first multi-cellular organisms evolved around 800 mya. Multi-cellular organisms are made from assemblages of eukaryotic cells. Unlike colonies consisting of cells that are all relatively similar, multi-cellular organisms have some cells that undergo extensive alterations in shape and function (differentiation). For example, in insects, some cells will differentiate into muscle cells, some into nerve cells, some into specialized cells of the digestive system and so on.

The ancestral multi-cellular organism spawned descendents that diversified and formed the major groups of multi-cellular animals. All multi-cellular animals alive today share the same basic eukaryotic cell type. This is an artifact of all multi-cellular animals being related through a common ancestor. Thus, we find that the cells of insects are similar to the cells of worms and mammals including humans. The sizes and types of cells in insects and elephants are quite similar. The much larger elephant has many more cells than the much smaller insect. The sizes of the cells are not smaller in smaller animals.

The diversity of multi-cellular organisms and the fossils they left behind expanded greatly between 542 and 488 mya. All major groups of animals have fossil ancestors dating to this period known as the "Cambrian Explosion." The evolution of multi-cellular organisms created a new level of biological complexity and opened many new biological niches for rapid evolution. Descendants of one of these groups, the arthropods, would eventually move onto land and form the branch of animals known as the insects.

The Arthropods

The word "arthropod" means "jointed appendage." In the ancestral arthropods, the original appendages were all legs used in walking on the ocean bottom or swimming. In modern arthropods, some of the jointed appendages are maintained as legs but others are modified to perform numerous functions other than locomotion. Appendages in the head are modified for feeding (mouthparts) or sensory perception (antennae). Appendages at the end of the abdomen are modified for mating.

An important characteristic of arthropods is an exoskeleton that contains the polymer, chitin. The exoskeleton provides protection for the internal organs and supports muscles used for movement. Chitin and the paired jointed appendages are important to the success of this group and have been preserved in their modern descendants.

Biologists classify all animals with paired jointed appendages and a chitinous exoskeleton as arthropods. These two traits do not appear in other groups of multi-cellular organisms. For example, worms and mollusks lack paired jointed appendages. Vertebrates that do have paired jointed appendages have an internal skeleton, not the chitinous arthropod exoskeleton.

> The State Fossil of Ohio is the trilobite, *Isotelus*. *Isotelus* fossils can be up to 2 feet in length. Trilobites deposited calcite and calcium phosphate in their exoskeleton. This made the exoskeleton less likely to degrade and produced large numbers of fossils. Over 17,000 species of trilobites have been described.

Like other groups of multi-cellular animals, the first arthropods were present in the pre-Cambrian period (over 542 mya). Much of what we know about early arthropods is derived from trilobite fossils. The oldest trilobites fossils are from the early Cambrian period (540 mya). The trilobites appear in the fossil record for about 300 million years. They became extinct about 250 mya.

The Trilobites incorporated calcium into their exoskeleton increasing their preservation. The hard armor suggests that trilobites lived in an environment where protection against predators was necessary. The legs of trilobites were probably used for walking on the ocean floor and for swimming.

Other groups of arthropods that evolved in the oceans include the crustaceans, the chelicerates, and marine myriapods. Fossils of these groups are not as numerous as the trilobites because their exoskeletons were more subject to deterioration and destruction. Although the trilobites went extinct about 250 mya, crustaceans, chelicerates, and myriapods have descendents that are living in the ocean today. Most marine arthropods are crustaceans and some including crabs, lobsters, and shrimp are familiar items in seafood restaurants. Horseshoe crabs are the most common marine chelicerate and numerous species of myriapods are marine.

7. Life Moves Onto Land

Before 475 mya, all life was in the ocean. Until oxygen released from photosynthesis substantially increased in the atmosphere, there would have been no ozone layer to protect life on land from destructive ultraviolet light. There were no land plants and therefore, nothing on land for animals to eat. Around 475 mya, plants first appeared on land. The first land plants were short compared to the dominant land plants today. These plants lacked the ability to transport water high above the soil. Therefore, the first plants were probably restricted to moist terrestrial areas similar to those inhabited by modern day mosses.

8. Arthropods Move Onto Land

Herbivores rapidly followed the plants onto land to exploit the new source of food. From the oceans, three groups of arthropods—crustaceans, chelicerates, and myriapods all followed plants onto land (Figure 1.3).

Examples from Major Arthropod Groups

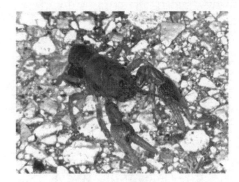
Crustacean: Crayfish

Crustacean: Pillbug

Chelicerates: A Spider

Trilobite (extinct)

Insects: A Beetle

Myriapod:
Millipede

Myriapod:House Centipede

Figure 1.3   Examples from the five largest groups of Arthopods. **Insects**, the largest group have 3 body regions and 3 pairs of legs. **Chelicerates** are named for their distintive pointed mouthparts (Chelicera). Adults have 2 body regions and 4 pairs of legs. **Crustaceans** are the most common marine arthropod and characterized by appendages that are divided into 2 parts (biramous) and 2 pairs of antennae. Myriapods have walking legs on each segment. **Millipedes** have 2 pairs of legs on each segment. **Centipedes** have 1 pair of legs on each segment. **Trilobites** are extinct arthropods that left large numbers of fossils (540 - 250 mya).

The **terrestrial chelicerates** include scorpions, ticks, spiders, and mites. Most of the chelicerates are predators, although some mites feed exclusively on plants. Spiders and mites are quite successful groups of terrestrial arthropods. However, they never achieved the diversity of insects. The relatively poor mobility is an important reason why chelicerates have never produced the diversity or number of species of insects.

Small aquatic animals can travel long distances by riding on the water currents. Small land animals are limited to moving relatively short distances by walking on the ground. Moving longer distances on land requires moving through the air. Spiders and mites both are capable of dispersing through the air. Spiders spin silk threads and "balloon" through the air with little control over take-off and landing. Tiny mites can be blown about by air currents. Spiders and mites have little control over the direction of transport or the location where they land. Large numbers die after the transport process because they are carried to a location that is unsuitable.

The spiders and mites are distinguished from insects by the presence of four pairs of legs on the adults and a body plan consisting of only two regions—the cephalothorax and abdomen. (Insects have three pairs of legs and three body regions.)

Terrestrial myriapods are represented by the millipedes and centipedes. The millipedes have two pairs of legs per segment and some species may have as many as 260 legs (Good thing they don't buy shoes!). Centipedes have many legs, but only one pair per segment. The millipedes and centipedes are easily recognized by the large numbers of walking legs. Millipedes primarily feed on dead and decaying plant material. Centipedes are predatory, feeding on small arthropods. Millipedes and centipedes are common and widespread and can often be found in leaf litter or under logs. The oldest land arthropod fossil is a millipede from about 425 mya.

The majority of extant marine arthropods are **crustaceans**. The majority of crustaceans live in the oceans. A few groups of crustaceans have successfully colonized land. The most numerous terrestrial crustaceans are the isopods, also known as, the sowbug, pillbug, or roly-poly. If you pick one up, it will roll into a ball and can roll off your hand. The pillbugs are subject to desiccation, inhabit moist areas under rocks, and typically avoid direct sunlight. They are distinguished from insects and spiders by their greater number of legs.

Movement of the isopods onto land is a separate event from another, far more successful movement of crustaceans onto land. These crustaceans were the ancestors of insects.

9. The First Insects

The insects evolved from a group of arthropods that had colonized land. Recent DNA evidence suggests that insects are most closely related to crustaceans. As more DNA evidence becomes available, the links between insects and the most closely related groups of crustaceans may be elucidated.

The early insects were wingless, limited in mobility, and likely not well adapted to terrestrial life. However, the first species to invade a new environment have the advantage of little or no competition. As adapted traits increased due to natural selection, insects became the most competitive of all the terrestrial animals.

Wingless, soil dwelling insects are present in large numbers, but the numbers of species in these groups is quite small compared to the insects as a group. However, these wingless insects had one key feature that was critical to the evolution of insects, a body region—the thorax—that is devoted to locomotion. The thorax contains the walking legs and muscles used for locomotion. Wings are extensions of the thorax of insects. For small insects that are blown through the air, even primitive extensions of the thorax could have helped them steer and land. Slight changes in muscle location could turn muscles used to move legs into muscles used to move the primitive wing.

10. Insects and Flight

Compared to walking, flying is a far more efficient means of movement. Flight enables small animals to move long distances relative to their size, endowing them with the ability to move within and between patches of habitat. Only the insects and two other groups of animals, birds and bats, have developed the capability of powered flight. Insects were the first animals to fly, an attribute that contributed to their diversity. Flight evolved very early in the evolution of insects, over 400 mya. Because insects were the first organisms with powered flight, they were able to diversify and occupy a number of niches that were not available to nonflying competitors. While there are a few species of insects that are primitively wingless, the vast majority of extant insect species are capable of powered flight, an indication of the importance of flight to the success of the insects.

Early Insects
Between 400 and 350 mya the insect fauna achieved a great diversity. Many of the earliest insects belonged to groups that have since gone extinct, but some groups of early insects are still extant and relatively unchanged. Cockroaches first appear in the fossil record by 350 mya. Fossils from 360 to 285 mya include dragonflies and crickets.

Insects were present on earth over 100 million years before the very first reptiles evolved around 310 mya. Some of the ancient insects reached an enormous size (by today's standards). Some dragonfly relatives that were present during the period 360 to 285 mya had wingspans over 2 feet (71 cm). Other giant arthropods in this period included a myriapod over 6 feet (2 m) long. The era of giant insects ended about 285 mya millions of years before dinosaurs evolved.

Extinctions and Speciation
In periods of relatively stable environmental conditions, new species appear infrequently, because new species typically have more difficulty competing for resources with well-adapted species. An abrupt change in environment (the cause of an extinction event) eliminates many species. This reduces competition for resources. The remaining species may undergo rapid change to adapt to the new environmental conditions. Extinctions leave many open niches (space and resources) for new species to occupy.

After a mass extinction, groups of animals that survive, (including some that were rare prior to the extinction) often undergo rapid speciation. Adaptations to the changed conditions or to better exploit the newly available resources will be favored post-extinction. New forms that can exploit unutilized resources have time and space free from competition to accumulate new adaptations.

Extinction Survivors
Scavengers, such as cockroaches are well suited to survive extinctions because they feed on dead or decaying organic matter. Typically, large changes in the environment do not eliminate their food sources. Thus cockroaches similar to those that existed 350 mya still survive today. Their food and microenvironment has not substantially changed over time.

The End of the Permian Extinction
Around 251 mya a massive extinction event eliminated over 95 percent of all terrestrial species. The mass extinction event marks the end of the Permian and beginning of the Triassic period. Two

groups of insects, the beetles and the flies survived the mass extinction and underwent a period of rapid speciation. To this day, beetles are the most numerous species of insect and the flies are one of the largest groups. During the Triassic period a new food source, the first coniferous plants, appeared. Another insect group to appear in the Triassic was the Hymenoptera, (the wasps). Most modern insect orders predate the dinosaurs. The earliest dinosaurs first appeared in the Triassic (245–210 mya).

Flowering Plants

The only large group of insects that does not have representatives in the Triassic is the Lepidoptera (butterflies and moths). The oldest Lepidoptera fossils are about 190 million years old. However, the great diversification of the Lepidoptera did not occur until after the evolution of the flowering plants during the Cretaceous (144–65 mya). Significant diversification of many insect groups occurred in response to the diversification of flowering plants. Many flowering plants are dependent on insects for pollination and many plants have evolved relationships with specific insect pollinators.

Dinosaur Extinction

An extinction event 65 mya (evidence suggests it was caused by an asteroid impact) eliminated the dinosaurs. Those insect species that depended on dinosaurs as a source of food also went extinct at that time. However, insects as a group were not greatly affected by this extinction. Almost all the insect groups present today had representatives that survived the extinction event of 65 mya.

Insect Fossils

Compared to some other animals, insects are not well preserved in the fossil record. Wings are far less likely to degrade than other insect body parts and many species of extinct insects are known only from their wings. Once coniferous plants appear, the fossil record for insects improves. Coniferous trees exude resin that can trap small animals such as insects and harden into a rock-hard material called amber. Amber is transparent and prevents the degradation of insect bodies. Many insects are preserved in amber exactly the way they were trapped millions of years ago.

Insects preserved in amber are used in the plot for the book and movie, *Jurassic Park*. In the story, scientists are able to recreate dinosaurs by rescuing their DNA and growing dinosaurs from that DNA. Where did they collect the dinosaur DNA? From mosquitoes trapped in amber that according to the story had been feeding on dinosaur blood.

Summary

The insects evolved from arthropod ancestors that followed the plants onto land over 425 mya. By 405 mya insects were flying through the air. Insects rapidly diversified and formed most of the groups present today over 200 mya. Other than the more recent addition of butterflies and moths, most insects groups have been in existence for well over 200 million years.

Name _____ Date _____

Chapter 1 Study Questions

1. How did the evolution of photosynthesis change the atmosphere of the earth and why is that important for life on land to be viable?

2. What group of multicellular organisms were the first to colonize the land and how did their success allow other groups of organism to leave the ocean and live on land?

3. What groups of arthropods were present in the ocean and which groups have successfully colonized the land? What characters can be used to distinguish the groups?

4. Current evidence suggests that insects evolved from crustacean ancestors that colonized the land. What features have insects evolved that have allowed insects to be more successful on land than crustaceans.

5. When did flight in insects evolve? Why is flight important to the success of insects?

6. How long were insects present on land before there were dinosaurs?

7. Mass extinction events are often followed by periods of rapid evolution. Why?

8. What groups of insects were present during the Permian and survived the end of the Permian extinction?

9. What large groups of insects evolved after the Permian period?

10. What is amber and why is important for investigating the history of insects?

Chapter 2

Collection, Curation, and Identification of Insects

Collecting and Curating Insects

Why Collect Insects?

Insect collections are critical to taxonomists who need to correctly identify insects. By collecting numerous species in one location, it is easier to compare their similarities and differences. Insects present at different times of the year or from separate locations can be compared side by side. Associated with collections are microscopes, deoxyribonucleic acid (DNA) sequencing and other tools that taxonomists use to distinguish features not seen with the naked eye.

For **hobbyists**, insect collections are a great way to learn how to identify common insects, appreciate their beauty, and share their hobby with others. In order to collect a diversity of insect species, hobbyists need to learn about the natural history and habits of insects. Baseline information on insect biology collected by hobbyists is an important contribution to science. Insects may also be used in displays and decorations. Artists may incorporate insects or insect parts such as wings into jewelry or other decorative items.

Collecting Insects

This chapter is meant to be an overview of the collection and curation process. For more information on how to start an insect collection, one of the many books on the subject such as *Arthropod Collection and Identification* by Gibb and Oseto.

Collecting insects can be as simple as picking up a resting insect and dropping it in a vial. However, not all insects are easy to collect, so entomologists have devised a series of tools—some more general and some very specific—for collecting insects. Nets, traps, attractants, and insect rearing are all used to collect specimens. A variety of tools are used to collect insects that are as varied as the habitats that contain insects.

Insect Nets
The insect net is the most commonly portrayed insect collecting device but is only one of many collecting tools. Insect nets are large, conspicuous, and readily identify people using the nets as entomologists. The insect net is a loose fabric that allows air to easily pass through, but tight enough weave that insects will not pass through. The net is a cone, circular at the open end, and tapering to point at a distance

that is at least twice as long as the diameter of the opening. The net has to be long enough to fold over itself and close the opening so the captured insects do not escape. The open end of the net is mounted on a rigid hoop (usually wire). The hoop is attached to a handle of convenient length.

Aerial Nets

Two common types of nets are aerial and sweep nets. The aerial nets are for the capture of flying insects and are commonly called butterfly nets. Insects are captured by rapidly moving the net over a flying or resting insect. As a tactic, it is much easier to stalk and capture a flying insect once it is resting rather than trying to knock it out of the air. The loose weave of the aerial net allows the collector to see the insect and prevent its escape during the transfer to the collecting jar.

Sweep Nets

Sweep nets are typically made of heavier material (unusually canvass) than aerial nets. Many small insects spend most of their time hidden in foliage. The sweep net is used to beat the foliage in a swinging motion that dislodges the insects from the plants. The dislodged insects are collected in the net and are easier to detect against the canvass background.

Traps

Insect collectors use a variety of traps. The design of effective traps is an art and is often based on knowledge of insect movement and behavior. Traps are a quick way of determining the presence or absence of insects in a location. If information is required for a single insect species, the trap may be specifically designed to capture the insect of interest and exclude other insects.

Traps may have a physical design that prevents the escape of an insect that enters the trap. For example, pitfall traps are containers with smooth sides that are buried so the open top of the container is even with the surroundings. Insects fall into the trap and are unable to climb the sides. Malaise traps are large tent-like pieces of netting mounted on poles that collect flying insects, primarily flies and wasps. The insects land on the trap and are funneled into a container at one end. In some cases an insecticide that kills insects is placed in the collection container of Malaise and other types of traps.

Some traps are coated with a sticky substance to immobilize insects. Sticky traps are most commonly used for monitoring insects rather than for collecting. To curate an insect stuck to a sticky trap, the adhesive must be carefully removed from the insect.

Traps may have attractants that lure insects. Pheromones are attractant odors that may be used for some moths, flies, and beetles. Rotting meat or dung may be used to attract carrion or dung feeding insects, respectively.

Blacklights

Many nocturnal insects are attracted to lights, especially the UV wavelengths. Entomologists can place a blacklight in front of a sheet. The insects land on the sheet and are easily collected. Blacklights are useful for collecting large numbers of species in a short time. The disadvantage is that they miss insects that do not fly or are not attracted to the light. Blacklights are sometimes incorporated into traps.

Aquatic Insects

A variety of devices are used to collect insects from water including nets, dip pans, and kick screens. The dip pan is a pan mounted on the end of a long stick. Mosquito larvae can be collected by maneuvering a dip pan beneath their location. These are commonly used by mosquito control campaigns to monitor mosquito larvae populations.

The kick screen is a square net on poles that is held above water at one end with the other end placed flush with the bottom of the lake or stream. One person can go upstream and overturn rocks to dislodge insects or herd them downstream onto the surface of the net. The insects cling to the net and are collected by lifting the net from the water.

Vacuums

Vacuums can be used to collect insects. Entomologists sometimes use large vacuums to literally suck all the insects out of an area. Tiny insects that are difficult to handle can be sucked into a container with a gentle vacuum called an aspirator.

Insect Curation

Killing insects

Insects preserved for collections need to be killed quickly to prevent damage. Ethyl acetate is a commonly used chemical agent that kills rapidly without discoloring the specimen.

Insect Preservation

Insect specimens are typically preserved in alcohol or dried on insect pins. Insects become very stiff when they dry. Sometimes it is necessary to place an insect in a humid jar (relaxing) to make it flexible enough to pin.

Pinning blocks are used for most insects. They can aid in setting the pin at the proper height with the insect perpendicular to the pin. Special spreading boards are used for curation of butterflies and moths. The wings are important in species identification and must be dried in an open position to display the important characteristics. The spreading board allows the butterfly to dry with its wings in a fully open position.

An insect pin (special pin that does not rust) is placed through the thorax of a dead insect on its right side. Pins are available in several sizes to match the size of the insect. Labels, small pieces of paper with information about the specimen, are attached to the shaft of the pin below the insect. The legs and antennae can be carefully moved to a desired position. The specimen is allowed to dry.

The pin is important for several reasons.
1. A pin provides a convenient **handle** for moving the insect. Dried insect specimens are brittle. Touching the specimen itself might damage the specimen. Dried specimens must be handled only by grasping the pin.
2. The pin can be combined with a stand to position a specimen motionless under a microscope.
3. A pin **protects** an insect by preventing contact with the box.
4. Information labels about the specimen are attached to the bottom of the pin. **Labels** contain information including the identity of the species, who collected it, and where and when it was collected.

Specimen boxes can contain from one to hundreds of pinned insect specimens depending on the size of the specimen. Many collectors use special specimen boxes called "drawers" because they are made to slide into racks in cabinets that hold multiple boxes. Specimen boxes have tightly closed lids to keep out pests. Boxes for display have glass lids. Specimens are arranged neatly within a box to conserve space.

Protection from pests. The most common pests of insect collections are dermestid beetles and ants. These insects will feed on dead insects. To deter insect pests, the boxes containing the dried specimens are sealed and typically contain an insecticide.

Alcohol specimens are placed in sealed vials with 70 percent ethanol. Specimens that lose their shape when pinned or are too small to pin (such as ants and aphids) are placed in alcohol. Insect larvae are more commonly preserved in alcohol than pinned. Soft-bodied insect larvae often do not maintain their shape when they dry. Alcohol is also used for preserving specimens for future investigation of DNA. The DNA is more stable in alcohol than in dried insect specimens.

Insect Identification

Insects can be more challenging to identify than other taxa because of the large numbers of species. Most people learn insect identification by taking classes or working with experienced collectors. There are numerous written guides and with the Internet, many pictorial guides available. Pictures can be misleading because of mimics. Often pictures are limited to only the most commonly encountered insects. Identification should always be confirmed by noting the key characteristics. Taxonomic keys are best for identifying insects. However, familiarity with the insect characters is important. For rare or closely related species, accurate identification of insects is challenging. Correct identification may require taxonomic experts.

Insect Museums

Collecting and preserving insects is an important endeavor. Scientific collections can contain millions of specimens. The Bishop Museum, one of the largest collections has over 14 million preserved insect specimens. The Purdue Entomology Collection (housed in the basement of Smith Hall) contains over 1.8 million preserved specimens representing over 100,000 species.

The value of specimens. More information can be gleaned from a collection of specimens than photos, digital images, or other methods of describing insects. Individual insects within a species vary. Collections can capture this variability better than a description, either verbal or pictorial. Photos, while useful, often fail to show some of the finer details of a specimen that taxonomists need for identification.

Collections allow entomologists to compare insects from different locations to note their similarities and differences and study variation within a population. Collections preserve insects over periods of time. Differences in insect species collected in a location decades ago from insects found in that location today can indicate changes in the environment. The presence or absence of key insect species can indicate a colder or warmer period or be related to environmental quality and pollution.

Preserving for the future. Descriptions are always incomplete. New tools such as DNA sequencing or advances in microscopy allow new ways of describing specimens. The specimens themselves are necessary to use the new tools. Scientists who collect insects for study will preserve some specimens for future reference as "voucher specimens." If questions arise concerning the insects used in the study, representatives of the specimens will be available.

Future Collections?

A picture may be "worth a thousand words" but a preserved specimen is "worth a thousand pictures." Three-dimensional computer holograms are being discussed as adjuncts to insect collections. However, the amount of time and data needed to preserve "digital insect specimens" at the highest resolution is not currently practical. Even as computer imaging improves, specimens will still be used as models for the improved imaging. Specimens are also useful as sources of DNA for molecular analysis. As computer imaging improves, it will be more widely used by taxonomists.

Insect Identification and Classification

The Classification System

As discussed in Chapter 1, all living organisms are related by descent with modification. The legacy of this process is the formation of a "Nested Hierarchy" of classification levels. The standard taxonomic classification, based on the binomial system of Linnaeus, is used for all living organisms (Table 2.1). Three examples are shown below:

	Monarch Butterfly	**Potato Beetle**	**Chimpanzee**
Kingdom:	Animalia	Animalia	Animalia
Phylum	Arthropoda	Arthropoda	Chordata
Class:	Insecta	Insecta	Mammalia
Order	Lepidoptera	Coleoptera	Primates
Family:	Nymphalidae	Chrysomelidae	Hominidae
Genus	*Danaus*	*Leptinotarsa*	*Pan*
Species	*plexippus*	*decemlineata*	*troglodytes*

TABLE 2.1 Comparison of the classification of some familiar animals.

Kingdom: At the top of the Hierarchy are very broad groups. For example, all animals from humans to sponges belong to the Kingdom "Animalia." At one time in their history, all animals shared a common ancestor. For animals, the last common ancestor was over 700 million years ago (mya). In the period from 600–500 mya, the descendants of the ancestral animal diversified and formed sub-groups called "Phyla."

Phylum: As shown in Table 2.1, the Phylum containing insects is Arthropoda, a name that refers to the "paired, jointed appendages." The evolutionary path that led to the phylum Arthropoda diverged from the path that led to Chordata, the phylum containing chimpanzees and humans over 700 mya.

Class: The phylum Arthropoda is divided into several Classes. Four of the five largest groups of arthropods evolved in the oceans before there were plants (food) on land. These include the trilobites (Class Trilobita, now extinct), the Class Crustacea (the most common extant marine organisms), Class Arachnida (including scorpions, spiders, and mites), and Myriapoda (including centipedes and millipedes). Once land plants appeared, crustaceans, arachnids, and myriapods all had species that independently adapted to land. Early in the history of terrestrial life, insects the largest group of arthropods evolved on land, presumably from crustacean ancestors. Insects are placed in their own Class, the Insecta.

Order: Each lower level in the classification contains fewer species that are more closely related and share a common ancestor that is more recent. The Class Insecta is divided into numerous orders.

Some of the largest orders are Lepidoptera (butterflies and moths), Diptera (flies), Hymenoptera (wasps), and Coleoptera (beetles). In the table above, the monarch belongs to the Lepidoptera, the order that includes all butterflies and moths.

Family: Family is a classification used to group organisms with many similar characteristics. For example, butterflies are divided into five major families. The monarchs belong to the Nymphalidae, the largest family of butterflies.

Genus and Species

The lowest classification levels are the *Genus* and *species*. A species is defined as "all individuals that are part of the same interbreeding population." A *Genus* typically contains groups of species that are very similar and closely related. Often an entomologist who is expert in a taxonomic group is required to distinguish among species in the same genus.

Scientific Names

Science requires precise communication that clearly identifies the organism under discussion. When scientists speak or write a *Genus* and *species* name, one and only one species is identified. Scientists around the world use the same *Genus* and *species* names even if the common names are different. For instance, in English we would write, "Monarch butterfly" but in German, it becomes "Monarch-Schmetterling." However, in both and English and German the scientific name, "*Danaus plexippus,*" is the same.

Some insect species share the same *species* name but have different *Genus* names. For instance, the house-fly is called *Musca domestica* and the house cricket is called *Acheata domestica*. By convention, a Genus name may only be used once. So the name, *Musca* is only used to describe a group of Diptera (flies) and is not used to describe any other group. This convention ensures that each species has a unique name.

Filing information. A unique identifier is valuable for filing information about a species. All scientific communications identify the *Genus* and *species* names of the organism studied. Attaching a name makes it easier for scientists to search and find information about a species. Unique names in documents make it easier to count numbers of species.

***Genus* and *species* conventions.** We distinguish the *Genus* and *species* name by placing them in *italics* (underlined if hand written). By convention, the *Genus* name is always capitalized and the *species* name is in lower case.

Common names suffer from numerous problems such as two distinct species having the same common name or a single species having numerous common names. There have been some attempts to standardize "common names by having organizations publish lists of acceptable common names." The Entomological Society of America is one such organization.

Common Name Conventions

Common names can create some confusion. For instance, a butterfly is not a true fly. To differentiate between insects that are true flies (Diptera) from insects that are not true flies, we write names of the true flies as two words, for instance, "horse fly" or "house fly." If the insect is not a true fly, its common name is written as a single word. For example, "butterfly," "firefly," or "dragonfly."

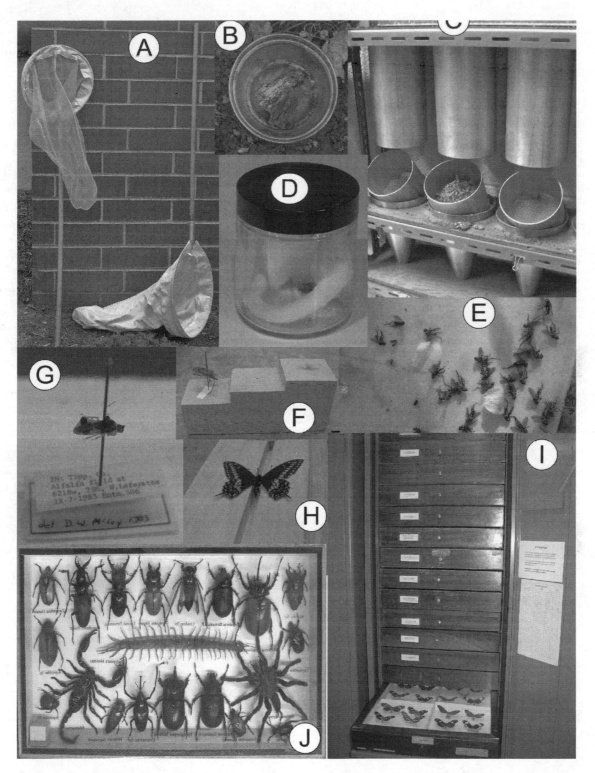

A. Aerial net for capture of flying insects (left) and sweep net for sweeping insects off foliage.   B. Pitfall trap for collecting insects running along the ground.   C. Berlese funnel for collecting soil dwelling arthropods.   D. Kill jar for rapidly killing captured insects. E. Sticky trap with flies stuck to the adhesive.   F. Pinning block for establishing uniform insect and label height.   G. Pinned insect showing labels and collection information.   H. Spreading board for curating Lepidoptera.   I. Cornell drawer and cabinet for storing multiple drawers.   J. Display collection of insects from Thailand.

Chapter 2 Study Questions

1. Why are scientific insect collections important?

2. List five tools an entomologist might use to collect insects and how they would be used.
   a.
   b.
   c.
   d.
   e.

3. What are three important differences in sweep nets and aerial nets and how they are used?
   a.
   b.
   c.

4. How are insect pins used in insect curation to protect specimens and organize information?

5. How are soft-bodied insects curated and why are they not mounted on pins?

6. List the classification hierarchy levels and indicate which ones contain both insects and mammals.

7. Why are both Genus and species names needed to uniquely identify an insect species?

8. How does the use of scientific names facilitate communication among scientists?

Chapter 3

Insect Development and Metamorphosis

The Insect Body Plan

The insect body plan consists of three regions: the head, the thorax, and the abdomen. The three separate regions and especially a single region, the thorax, devoted to locomotion may have been important for the evolution of flight.

The head of the insect contains sensory receptors for gathering information about the environment, large ganglia of the nervous system responsible for processing the information and the opening to the alimentary system along with the mouthparts for capturing food and pushing it into the mouth.

Sensory Systems

The insect head contains structures dedicated to gathering visual and odor information. Insect vision and olfaction are discussed in more detail subsequent chapters. The antennae are the primary olfactory organs of the insect. Odors are caused by chemicals that are present in the air. Molecules are swept from the air by the antennae and interact with odor receptors in the antenna interior. The compound eyes are the primary receptor for visual information. Simple eyes (called ocelli in adult insects) may give information about light direction, intensity, and day length.

The insect head contains sensory hairs that are sensitive to touch and to wind movements. These receptors are important for insect orientation and other behaviors. The insect mouthparts contain taste receptors that provide information about the food the insect consumes.

Information Processing

The insect head contains large ganglia for processing the olfactory information from the antennae, the visual information from the compound eyes and a ganglion responsible for integration of information and command and control of behaviors. An additional ganglion processes the sensory information from the taste receptors and controls and coordinates the muscles that move the mouthparts.

Insect Mouthparts

Insect have three pairs of mouthparts that manipulate the food: the mandibles, the maxillae, and the labium. The mouthparts are derived from modified legs. In the grasshopper, the mandibles are adapted for cutting leaves. Leaf pieces cut by the mandibles fall onto the labium, which forms a platform in front of the mouth. The maxillae push the food into the mouth. In other insects, the mouthparts may be modified in a variety of ways. Mandibles may be modified for spearing prey or into a tube for sucking liquids. Specific modification of the mouthparts will be discussed in the context of the biology of the insect orders.

The Thorax

The thorax of the insect is devoted to locomotion. The thorax consists of three segments, each with a pair of legs. Flying insects may have two pair of wings located on the hind two segments of the thorax.

The Abdomen

The abdomen is specialized for processing food (digestion/absorption) and (in adults) for reproduction. The segments of the abdomen of insects lack paired jointed appendages with the exception of the reproductive structures at the end of the abdomen used in copulation and egg laying. Some insects have cerci, or long appendages, containing sensory organs on the terminal segment of the abdomen. Cerci are typically sensitive to movements of air (or water movement if the insects are aquatic) and warn the insect of approaching predators.

Molting and Metamorphosis

The growth and development of insects has been a source of wonder that has captivated poets, scientists, writers, and the public for ages. The metamorphosis of a caterpillar into a beautiful butterfly is truly a wonder to behold. The idea of a plain, somewhat ugly caterpillar turning into a beautiful butterfly with the ability to glide gracefully through the air is a source of inspiration. Metamorphosis is a true beauty of nature that can be appreciated at the aesthetic level. Understanding the process of this amazing transformation has its own appeal.

Insects Eggs

All insects start life as an egg. The insect egg contains nutrients that we call the "yolk" (like chicken eggs). All the nutrients needed to produce an insect larva (proteins, carbohydrates, lipids, vitamins, minerals, and water) are contained within the yolk. A single female reproductive cell, the oocyte, is present in the egg when it is produced.

Fertilization

Females obtain sperm from males during mating and store the sperm. Mating may occur prior to egg production. Each egg has an opening to allow the sperm to enter. The sperm enters the egg and the genetic material from the male and female combine in the single reproductive cell. Fertilization typically takes place shortly before the egg is laid. The fertilized cell (with a full complement of chromosomes) divides for many generations to produce thousands of cells. The cells start as a disk floating on top of the yolk. As cells divide, they eventually incorporate all the yolk.

Insect Development

The caterpillar or tiny grasshopper that hatches from an egg is the result of cells that grow divide, and differentiate in an orchestrated process. How are cells working in concert able to produce an entire animal?

Gradients in the egg. The insect egg is not uniform. Nutrients are distributed in a non-uniform manner. From the start, insect cells occupying different locations within the egg receive different signals. Cells release chemicals into the egg that create chemical gradients. Cells communicate directly with neighbor cells. The combination of signals each cell receives depends on its location in the egg.

Each cell receives chemical signals at its location in the egg that "tell" the cell when to grow, when to divide and when to differentiate into a specific cell type such as a muscle cell or a nerve cell. All the information needed to create every type of cell is contained in the genes (DNA) of each cell. The chemical signals at each location "tell" the each cell which genes to turn on and which ones to turn off.

Local signals and feedback. Local chemical signals in the area where a leg should grow will cause some groups of cells to grow and divide in the shape of an insect leg. In the antenna area, groups of cells will grow and divide in the shape of an antenna. In the digestive system area cells will grow and divide into the organs of the digestive system.

The complex process of growing a complete animal from a single cell is orchestrated by the cells themselves. Cells grow, divide, differentiate, and even die in response to other cells and the chemical signals they release. The genetic information within each cell gives instructions on how each cell should respond within its own environment in a remarkable system of feedback between genes and environment.

The differentiation of cell is just as amazing as the metamorphosis of a caterpillar into a butterfly. A plain round stem cell can differentiate into an elongated nerve cell with its intricate branches and connections with other cells. Another plain round cell can differentiate into an elongated muscle cell filled with strands of protein.

The insect itself is the sum of the underlying cells that comprise the insect. The same cells that can grow and differentiate to form a caterpillar can under the influence of a different set of signals grow and differentiate to form a butterfly.

Larval growth. Once the cells of the egg have produced an insect, the larva will hatch and begin to live on its own and consume food. The insect grows because the food it assimilates is used by cells to grow and divide. This process is similar in all animals. Animals grow because the cells that comprise the animal are growing, dividing and differentiating.

Continuous and discontinuous growth. Growth and development in insects has some differences with growth and development in humans. Growth in humans is continuous from infant to adulthood. Humans have an internal skeleton and growth can be continuous. Developmental changes are gradual and occur over days and years.

While some growth in insects is continuous, the amount insects can grow is limited by ability of their exoskeleton to expand. As the insect grows, it will eventually reach a size where its old exoskeleton is no longer adequate. When it reaches its limit, the insect will shed its old exoskeleton and replace it with a new and larger exoskeleton in a process called **molting**.

Steps in the Molting Process

Step 1. Release of the molting hormone, ecdysone starts the process

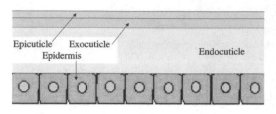

Step 2. The old cuticle separates from the epidermal cells

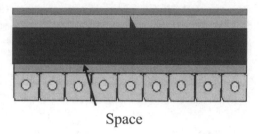

Space

Step 3. New epi-cuticle is secreted into the space

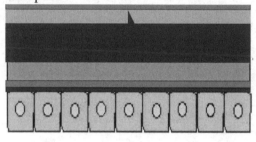

Step 4. Molting fluid secreted into the space

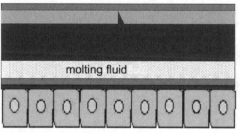

Step 5. Molting fluid digests the old cuticle

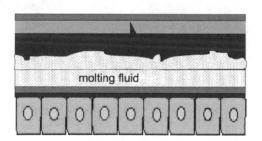

Step 6. Only a very thin part of the old is not digested.

Ecdysial Line

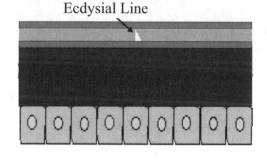

Step 7. The old cuticle breaks along the very thin ecdysial line

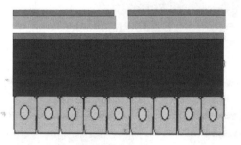

Step 8. Tanning-The new cuticle hardens

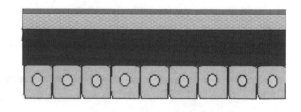

The Exoskeleton

The exoskeleton of an insect consists of a single layer of cells (the epidermis) and their secretions (cuticle and epicuticle). The secreted cuticle is the thickest layer that creates the structure. The epicuticle is the thin outermost coating of the exoskeleton.

The Epidermis. The epidermis is the living part of the exoskeleton. The cells border the internal insect fluid, the hemolymph, on the inside. The cells acquire nutrients from the hemolymph that are used to produce the secretions that create the cuticle. The production of cuticle and the secretions of the epidermis are under the control of hormones that circulate in the hemolymph.

Cuticle. The outer parts of the exoskeleton, the cuticle and epicuticle, are made from secretions of the epidermal cells. A similar process in humans produces our toenails and fingernails. Fingernails are mostly composed of a protein, keratin, that is secreted by the underlying epidermal cells.

Like human fingernails, the insect cuticle is a secretion, but the materials are different and have different properties. Insects use a variety of components in different areas of their cuticle. For instance, areas of the insect cuticle that are very hard have a lot of protein called sclerotin. Areas that require a lot of flexibility such as the joints of the legs contain another type of protein called resilin.

The cells of the epidermis receive signals at their location that indicate which protein to secrete. If the epidermis cells are in a joint, they will mostly secrete resilin. If the cells underlie a hard surface, the cells will mostly secrete sclerotin. Sclerotin can be made very hard by a process (cross-linking) called tanning. The cuticle is thicker in some locations and thinner in others. The insect can bend and move in the thin areas, but is very stiff in thicker areas. Some thin areas can be hardened and quite sharp (such as mouthparts that must cut hard materials).

Insects are capable of producing cuticle with a wide variety of properties. There are dozens of proteins that are used in the cuticle in different combinations. The thickness of the cuticle can be controlled. The degree of hardening due to tanning can be varied. The cuticle conforms to the shape of the underlying cells. Cells can grow outward to form spines or ridges or grow inward to form apodemes for structural support and muscle attachment.

Chitin. In addition to proteins, the cuticle contains strands of the polysaccharide, chitin, that is embedded in a protein matrix. Chitin is a polymer (a long chain) that can cross-link to other polymers including proteins. The cross-linking provides structure and resistance to tearing. Chitin reinforces the protein matrix to prevent tearing the same way that rebar or wire mesh is used to reinforce concrete. The chitin fibers are secreted in layers that are oriented at different angles. The same principle is used in making plywood. In plywood, the grain of each alternate layer is oriented in a different direction. This provides additional resistance to tearing.

Chitin is a key to producing a successful exoskeleton with jointed appendages. Chitin production was a key to success at the very beginning of arthropod evolution and is produced by all extant arthropods.

The epicuticle is a thin outer layer that is secreted on top of the protein and chitin layer that makes up the cuticle. The epicuticle is the part of an insect that we touch when we pick up an insect. The secretions that comprise the epicuticle differ among insects. For example, German cockroaches have an epicuticle that is "greasy" to touch and transfers if rubbed. Other insects such as beetles have a very hard surface that is not easily removed.

All epicuticle contains a lipid layer. The lipid of the epicuticle is either a wax or grease that is a barrier to water loss. We use the same principle when we apply waterproofing grease or oil to leather boots. The grease or oil repels water and keeps water from soaking through the leather. In the same way, the wax or grease of the insect epicuticle repels water and prevents the water from leaving the insect. Preventing dehydration is especially important in very small animals. Small animals such as insects have higher surface area to body mass ratios than larger animals. In other words, insects contain less water (body mass is mostly water) per unit of surface area than larger animals. Insects will desiccate (dry out) if the epicuticle is compromised.

Sensory Receptors. The insect exoskeleton is not a smooth sheet but has hairs and sensory cells that protrude through the cuticle. Insects have numerous sensory cells in their exoskeleton that are responsive to touch, wind, smell or taste. The cells of the receptors are located in the same layer as the epidermal cells but their projections extend through the cuticle to the outside. The receptors allow the insect to collect information from its environment.

Cuticle and Growth

Parts of the insect exoskeleton are very hard plates that provide protection or anchor muscles, but cannot be expanded. Between the hard plates are more flexible areas of the cuticle that can expand as the insect grows. Once the flexible areas of the cuticle are fully expanded, the insect must produce a new exoskeleton before it can grow further.

Producing A New Exoskeleton

Insects cannot survive without their cuticle. Therefore, they must produce their new cuticle beneath the old one. Producing a new cuticle requires a complex series of steps.

The first step in producing a new cuticle is a separation of the old cuticle from the cells of the underlying epidermis. The epidermal cells will secrete a new cuticle into this space underneath the old cuticle. New epicuticle and a thin layer of cuticle are first secreted into the space.

Digestive enzymes are secreted into the space between the new epicuticle and the old cuticle. Once the initial layers of the new cuticle are secreted, the digestive enzymes are activated and begin to digest the old cuticle from the inside out. The chitin and proteins that make up the old cuticle are digested into component sugars and amino acids. These building blocks are taken up by the epidermis and incorporated into the new cuticle. As the old cuticle is digested the new cuticle increases.

The outermost layer of the old cuticle is protected from digestion and will remain intact until it is time for the insect to molt. The digestion process makes the old cuticle very thin with an even thinner line of weakness for the insect to escape.

Molting

Molting is the process of shedding the old cuticle. When it is time to molt, the insect will move its muscles and fluids to exert pressure against the old cuticle. The digestion of the old cuticle leaves weak lines that allow the old cuticle to split smoothly. The old cuticle typically splits along the top of the back of the insect thorax. The insect must then crawl out of its old cuticle. The space between the old and new cuticle contains fluid that helps the insect extricate itself. The process of molting is difficult. Failure to molt properly can cause insect mortality.

The new cuticle is larger than the old cuticle. The new cuticle must be folded when it is formed, then expanded to a much larger size after the insect molts. Question: If the new head capsule of a caterpillar is larger than the old one, where does it form?

Tanning

The new cuticle of the insect is very light colored and flexible. The flexibility helps the insect escape from its old cuticle. However, in order to function, the new cuticle must harden or "tan." Tanning involves cross-linking some of the protein and chitin polymers in the cuticle. (Cross-linking is a similar to the cross-linking process that occurs with epoxy. When first mixed, epoxy is fluid and malleable. However, after cross-linking occurs, the epoxy becomes hard. Tanning works the same way but with protein and chitin as the polymers instead of epoxy.)

The tanning process is orchestrated by hormones that are released only after the insect is free of the old cuticle. Tanning can continue for several days after a molt. A newly molted insect will appear light in color. The cuticle is flexible and the insect is more fragile and easily damaged. Insect movements are most efficient when the cuticle is sufficiently hardened. Adult insects that are newly molted are often unable to fly until they harden. Often, molting occurs at night out of the view of hungry predators. As tanning (cross-linking) progresses, the coloration increasingly darkens. The darkening occurs because the cross-linked proteins are darker in color than the proteins that are not cross-linked.

Metamorphosis

In a process called metamorphosis, insects change from one type of life stage to another. Most insects including beetles, flies, wasps, and moths have complete metamorphosis. Insects with complete metamorphosis have four developmental stages: the egg, larva, pupa, and adult. Some insects such as grasshoppers and cockroaches have incomplete metamorphosis. Insects with incomplete metamorphosis have only egg, larva, and adult stages and do not have a pupa stage.

Incomplete metamorphosis. Insects with incomplete metamorphosis typically undergo a series of larval molts and a final molt that produces a fully developed adult. Adult insects do not molt. The larvae of insects with incomplete metamorphosis typically resemble miniature adults. The mouthparts of the larvae and adults are the same and the food is often the same. In larvae with incomplete metamorphosis, the wings typically develop externally as wing buds on the thorax. With each molt, the wing buds increase in size relative to the size of the larva. Before the molt to adult, the adult wings form folded inside the wing buds. When the adult emerges from the last larval cuticle, the wings will be expanded and hardened.

Complete metamorphosis. Insects with complete metamorphosis will typically undergo a series of larval molts. Each larval stage closely resembles the previous stage, except for size. There are no external wing pads or signs of wing development in larvae with complete metamorphosis. After the final larval stage, insects with complete metamorphosis will molt to a pupal stage. The pupal stage

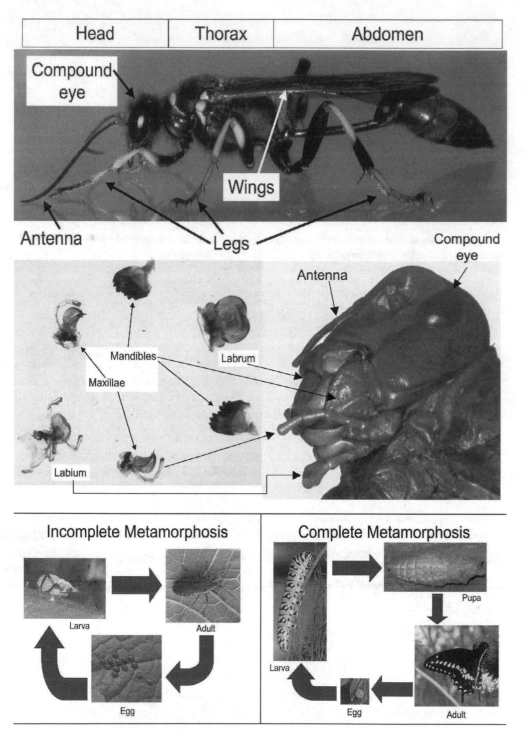

Top: Wasp with body regions labeled. The head contains the mouthparts and organs of olfaction and vision. The thorax is adapted to locomotion- walking and flight. The abdomen contains internal organs of digestion and reproduction.

Middle: Head (right; (left antenna removed)) and dissected mouthparts (left) of a grasshopper.

Bottom: Life cycles of the squash bug (left) demonstrating incomplete metamorphosis and black swallowtail butterfly (right) demonstrating complete metamorphosis. Incomplete metamorphosis lacks a pupa stage.

is often intermediate in form between the larva and the adult and does not resemble either very closely. Within the pupa, many of the cells will die and release their contents. These nutrients will be the building blocks for the cells of the adult insect. The adult will be formed from imaginal disk cells (clusters of cells that are dormant during larval development). The adult insect is formed from imaginal disk cells in much the same way that the cells in an egg grow divide and differentiate to form the newly hatched larva.

The process of metamorphosis allows the adults to have very different characteristics from the larvae. Although beetles typically have similar chewing mouthparts in both larvae and adults, caterpillars (larvae) have chewing mouthparts while butterflies and moths (adults) have long tubes for sucking the liquid nectar from flowers. There are no signs of wings in the larvae, but the adults emerge from their pupae with fully formed wings. The transformation from caterpillar to butterfly is indeed a wonder to behold. Metamorphosis requires that many of the old insect cells die and the adult insect be remade from the components of the old cells by entirely different cells.

What Controls Metamorphosis?

Metamorphosis in insects is under hormonal control the same way that adult development in humans is controlled by our hormones. However, the hormones are different. Humans have hormones such as testosterone and estrogen that control development. Insects use juvenile hormone.

Juvenile hormone. Insect larvae make relatively large amounts of juvenile hormone (JH). JH activates genes for larval traits and suppresses genes for adult traits. JH keeps the larval cells from dying and suppresses development of the adult cells. As long as juvenile hormone is present during a molt, an insect will molt to a larger larva. If juvenile hormone is absent during the molt, the insect will molt to an adult (incomplete metamorphosis) or to a pupa (complete metamorphosis).

It is possible to artificially treat insects with JH or to remove the glands that produce JH. Treating a caterpillar with JH will cause the caterpillar to molt to a larger caterpillar. The larger caterpillar will produce a larger than normal moth. Removing the glands that produce the JH will cause an insect to molt to an adult or pupa instead of a larger larva. The adults will be much smaller than normal. Typically, premature molting or extra molts will lead to deformities that leave the insect sterile.

Why Do Insects Have Metamorphosis?

Metamorphosis allows larvae to be better adapted to feeding and adults better adapted for reproduction and dispersal. Changes in larval characteristics that greatly enhance growth and feeding can happen without affecting the characteristics of the adult. Evolution of adult characteristics that enhance mating finding, reproduction and egg laying do not affect larval adaptations.

The most successful insects (largest numbers of species) have complete metamorphosis. Because the larvae and adults can be very different in appearance, larvae and adults can each be better adapted to each environment, rather than having a single hybrid form that is less well adapted to either environment. Larvae are often specialized to grow very rapidly in specialized habitats. Adults must fly to find mates and disperse efficiently. Insects with complete metamorphosis have larvae and adults that are well adapted to these specializations.

Metamorphosis: More Than Appearances

It is not just appearances that change between larvae and adults. The behaviors and the underlying nervous system of larvae and adults must undergo enormous changes. Adults need behaviors for flying. Larvae lack wings and don't fly. Larvae with chewing mouthparts need different feeding behaviors than adults with sucking mouthparts. Legless maggots have crawling behaviors that are not used by adult flies with walking legs. Larvae need a different set of muscles and nerves to control the muscles than adults. During complete metamorphosis, the muscle and nervous systems are radically transformed.

Metamorphosis is truly amazing in more ways than meet the eye.

Chapter 3 Study Questions

1. What are the primary functions of the insect head?

2. What is the primary function of the insect thorax?

3. What are the primary functions of the insect abdomen?

4. What are the major layers of the insect exoskeleton?

5. What are the primary components of the insect cuticle?

6. What is the importance of the insect exocuticle?

7. What are the steps in producing a new exocuticle?

8. What is the difference between complete and incomplete metamorphosis?

9. Why are insects with complete metamorphosis more successful than insects with incomplete metamorphosis?

10. What is the role of juvenile hormone in metamorphosis?

Chapter 4

Inside the Insect

Growth and Reproduction

Insects must get all their nutrition by consuming the cells or secretions of other organisms. The nutrients that can be effectively and efficiently used are assimilated and the remainder excreted.

Although all cells from all organisms contain the same nutrients, those nutrients may be present in different relative quantities. Additionally, those nutrients may be defended by the organism with chemical toxins or other barriers. Insects may be prevented from utilizing many organisms as sources of food because of these barriers. Therefore, many insects specialize on those organisms that they can effectively and efficiently process.

The digestive system of an insect species is often adapted to a single food or a small group of foods. For example, the digestive system of the caterpillar of butterflies is adapted to processing plant leaves, the digestive system of the praying mantis is adapted to processing insect prey and the digestive system of the adult female mosquito is adapted to processing a blood meal. The advantages of adaptation to a single (or only a few) food sources has led to diversification of insect species and to profound differences among insects in their digestive systems.

Overview of Digestion

Insect food typically consists of organisms, their tissues, and/or their secretions. Tissues consist of groups of cells. Cells contain water, minerals, and complex associations of biomolecules including carbohydrates, proteins, nucleic acids, and lipids. To be ingested, tissues have to be chewed into "bite-sized" ingestible pieces. The cells within the tissue are disrupted, their contents released and the complex biomolecules reduced to basic building blocks that can be used by the insect cells. The basic building blocks needed by insect cells (and all cells) are amino acids (used to make proteins), sugars (used to make complex carbohydrates) lipids such as fatty acids and sterols (used to make cell membranes, hormones and complex lipids), and nucleotides (used to make RNA and DNA). Once the food is digested, the basic building blocks, vitamins and minerals, can be absorbed and assimilated.

Absorption

The nutrients released during digestion are transported out of the digestive system and into the hemolymph (blood) of the insect. The nutrients circulate in the hemolymph and can be absorbed by the cells of the insect.

Oxygen

In addition to ingested nutrients (food and water), cells need oxygen to produce energy. Energy to power the cell is captured in a complex cellular process that combines oxygen with small molecules such as sugars. Insects must deliver oxygen to each of their cells where the oxygen is used.

What Is Inside An Insect?

The major systems inside the insect are responsible for food digestion and processing, respiration, circulation, excretion, communication (nerves), movement (muscles), and reproduction.

Digestive System

Food enters the digestive system through the oral opening (mouth), and travels through a series of digestive organs that store, grind, and digest the food, absorb the nutrients, and eliminate the waste. The waste passes to the outside of the insect through its anus.

Mouthparts

Food processing starts with the mouthparts. Mouthparts are modified legs (three pairs) that exist outside the true mouth or opening to the food canal. In chewing insects such as the grasshopper, the anterior pair of legs is modified into mandibles, the median pair modified into maxillae, and the posterior pair modified into the labium. In grasshoppers (that chew leaves), the scissors-like mandibles cut small pieces from leaves. The leaf pieces fall onto the labium (or floor of the pre-oral cavity) and are pushed back into the digestive system by the maxillae.

Insect mouthparts are commonly modified for ingestion of specific types of food such as plant leaves, stems, seeds, or roots, plant, or animal secretions or insect prey. In some insects, mouthparts are modified as sucking mouthparts, straw-like tubes for imbibing liquids. In the group Hemiptera, all the members have sucking mouthparts.

Salivary Glands

Salivary glands produce a fluid that may contain a suite of digestive enzymes (proteins), lipids, surfactants, water, and other materials useful for feeding and digestion. The salivary glands may be present in the head, or extend into the thorax and abdomen of some insects.

Many sucking insects inject saliva into their food. The saliva digests the food extra-orally. For example, predatory bugs, that insert their sucking mouthparts into prey, inject saliva that immobilizes their prey, and digests the prey within its cuticle. The insides of the prey are liquefied and ingested through the sucking mouthparts of the bug. All that remains of the prey is the empty cuticle.

Chewing insects often add saliva to the food they ingest. The saliva lubricates the food so it can move through the alimentary system. Enzymes in the saliva start the digestion process.

Pharynx

The pharynx is the first section of the insect alimentary system that food contacts after it enters the mouth. The pharynx pumps or pushes food into gut. For chewing insects that ingest solid food, the muscles of the pharynx will contract from anterior to posterior and force the food into the esophagus. In some sucking insects, the pharynx is a pump that can pump liquids out of the food, through the straw-like mouthparts and into the digestive system. The sucking action is similar to sucking a drink through a straw.

Esophagus

The head has little room for digestive organs. The thorax of many insects is filled with muscles for locomotion. The digestive organs are typically located in the abdomen. Food travels from the head to the abdomen, through a tube called the esophagus. The esophagus in insects has the same function as the human esophagus.

The lumen of the esophagus (side facing the food) is lined with cuticle that protects the insect from abrasive or sharp food particles. Food spends relatively little time in the esophagus and little digestion or absorption of food occurs. The esophagus is ringed by muscles that contract to force the food through the tube. The muscles function in the same way that squeezing a tube of toothpaste forces the solid material through the tube. Food is "squeezed" through the esophagus and into the crop.

Crop

The crop is an extendable pouch that stores food. The crop is typically located in the abdomen and may expand when food is consumed. In some insects, filling the crop causes the abdomen to swell. In other insects, the abdomen contains air sacs that shrink as the crop expands. Many insects are capable of consuming food much faster than it can be digested. This allows insects to feed intermittently. Intermittent feeding is important because dinner for insects can be interrupted by the arrival of predators. Some insects hide from predators by only feeding at night or emerging to feed for a brief period, then returning to hiding. While the insect is hiding, food stored in the crop can be fed slowly into the rest of the digestive system so the nutrients can be efficiently processed.

For example, female mosquitoes typically spend only a brief period on their host. Lingering on the host increases the risk of death or injury. Mosquitoes bite the host and rapidly fill their crop with blood. Once the crop is full, they fly off to digest their food in relative safety.

Proventriculus

Grasshoppers and many chewing insects have a grinding organ called the proventriculus. The inside of the proventriculus has hard cuticle with sharp edges. The muscles of the proventriculus contract to cut the food into tiny pieces creating a "mash." The fine pieces are more easily penetrated by digestive enzymes.

Gastric Caeca

The gastric caeca are blind pouches (diverticuli) that are connected to the main alimentary canal at the junction of the proventriculus and the midgut. The gastric caeca are a single layer of cells thick. These cells are capable of absorbing some nutrients, (especially sugars) from the inside of the alimentary canal and transporting them into the hemolymph. The function of the gastric caeca of insects (nutrient absorption) is similar to the appendix in some vertebrate herbivores such as rabbits.

Midgut

The midgut is the primary digestive organ of the insect. The cells of the midgut secrete digestive fluid that disrupts the lipid membranes of cells in the food, and breaks down proteins into amino acids and carbohydrates into simple sugars. Cells of the midgut have transporters that move nutrients such as amino acids, sugars, lipids, nucleotides, vitamins, and minerals from the alimentary canal, through the cells, and into the insect hemolymph (blood).

The cells of the midgut may act as a barrier to prevent bacteria and viruses from entering the hemolymph of the insect. The digestive fluid can kill many of the potential pathogens. Cells of the midgut also have a role in protecting against toxic chemicals. Many plants, fungi and animals contain toxins that could harm the insect. The midgut cells may contain enzymes that can detoxify toxic chemicals. The toxins are metabolized into harmless products that can be eliminated from the insect. Detoxification enzymes in the insect midgut allow some insects to feed on plants that are very toxic to people.

Hindgut

The hindgut of the insect processes the waste (food that is not digested and absorbed) and prepares it for excretion. Important nutrients and vitamins are recovered from the waste and transported to the hemolymph. The hindgut in some insects removes water from the food to produce a dried pellet. The polite term for waste products of insects is "frass."

Malpighian Tubules

The Malpighian tubules are tube-like structures attached to the digestive system at the junction between the midgut and the hindgut. Each tube has a central canal that is encircled by a single row of cells. An insect may contain only a few Malpighian tubules or hundreds, depending on the species.

The Malpighian tubules are the functional equivalent of the vertebrate kidney. The cells of the Malpighian tubules separate the waste products to be excreted from nutrients that are returned to the hemolymph. Waste products from the hemolymph flow through the central canal of the Malpighian tubules as urine. The urine enters the hindgut where it is processed for elimination with the rest of the food waste.

How is the waste produced? In processing food, insects may absorb toxins or other components of food that cannot be utilized. During normal activity, components of insect cells may be damaged and need to be eliminated. The waste products circulate in the hemolymph and are filtered from the blood by the Malpighian tubules.

The Hemocoel

The hemocoel is a body cavity located between the gut and the epidermis of the insect. The hemocoel is filled with hemolymph (the insect blood). The hemolymph of insects does not travel in veins and arteries; it fills the hemocoel or body cavity. This arrangement is called an "open circulatory system." (Humans have a "closed circulatory system." Human blood does not leave the veins, arteries, and capillaries unless the system is damaged.)

The open circulatory system is well suited to relatively small animals like insects. Terrestrial insects are subject to dehydration and an open circulatory system allows the limited space available to maximize water content. In addition to water, the hemolymph contains minerals, vitamins, proteins, other complex macromolecules, and free moving cells. There are a diversity of hemolymph cells (hemocytes) that have a number of important roles such as forming clots to plug puncture wounds or attacking invading pathogens. Unlike vertebrate hemocytes, insect hemocytes do not transport oxygen.

Dorsal Organ

Insects have a "pump" called the dorsal organ. The dorsal organ pumps hemolymph from the thorax and abdomen into the head. The hemolymph flows back into the thorax outside of the dorsal organ. The circulation moves nutrients and hormones.

Oxygen Not Carried by Hemolymph

Unlike human blood, insect hemolymph does NOT carry oxygen. Humans have a protein in their blood cells (hemoglobin) that carries oxygen from the lungs to the cells and carbon dioxide from the cells to the lungs. Insects have a respiratory system that is separate from the circulatory system.

Fat Body

Fat body cells are the primary metabolic cells of an insect. These cells are called "fat body" because they contain a relatively high lipid content. The fat body consists of masses of cells that are dispersed throughout the hemocoel. Fat body processes nutrients, makes the yolk of eggs and performs numerous metabolic functions. The fat body of insects has a similar function to the human liver.

Respiration

The insect respiratory system consists of a series of tubes or "trachea" that open to the outside through valves called spiracles. Oxygen enters and carbon dioxide leaves through the spiracles located on the sides of the insect thorax and abdomen. The spiracles have muscles that can open the valves to allow gas exchange and close the valves to limit water loss.

The trachea are tubes that extend from the spiracles and branch repeatedly to carry oxygen to every cell in the insect body. The ever smaller trachea terminally branch into tiny tracheoles that are intimately associated with cells. The tracheoles are the primary sites of gas exchange between individual cells and the tracheal system. Oxygen enters a cell from the tracheole and carbon dioxide is released into the tracheole for transport to the outside.

Many insects are small enough that gas exchange can occur by simple diffusion of gas through the trachea. Some large insects such as locusts may have air sacs that can pump air in and out of the trachea.

Nervous System

Nerves are cells that specialize in communication and coordination of activity. Nerve cells receive signals in one location and deliver signals to another location. Interconnected networks of nerve cells called ganglia process signals, make decisions, and control behaviors through the coordination of the muscle movements that produce the behavior. Information from the ganglia is communicated to muscles through a network of motor nerves. Motor nerves control the timing, rate and extent of muscle movements. For example, a grasshopper jumps when the nerves in a ganglia send a message to the motor nerves, that coordinates the contraction of leg muscles to produce a jump.

As is discussed in more detail elsewhere in your reading, insects possess a variety of sensory receptors that collect information about the environment (temperature, light odor, touch, etc). Sensory receptors are connected to the nervous system by sensory nerves. The sensory nerves communicate the information from the receptors to ganglia for processing.

The central nervous system of insects consists of several ganglia connected by two major nerve chords. The primary insect nerve chord is on the ventral side of the insect. (In humans, our nerve chord is located in the spine on our dorsal side.)

The head has ganglia that receive and process visual, olfactory and taste information and control the mouthparts and the salivary glands. The ganglia in the thorax control the legs and the wings and receive information from receptors in the legs, wings, and thorax. Ganglia in the abdomen control mating and egg laying and receive information from receptors in the abdomen.

In the insect nervous system, the behavior "programs" for moving muscles are present in the ganglia of that segment. For example, the forelegs of an insect are attached to the prothoracic (first thoracic) segment. The movements of the insect forelegs are controlled by the ganglion in the prothorax. This differs from humans who store the information for controlling leg and arm movements in the head. Thus a headless insect may still be capable of walking. A headless male mantis is still capable of mating. This is because the ganglia in the thorax (walking) or abdomen (mating) contain all the information needed to control the behavior.

Insect Muscles

Insects have two classes of muscles: visceral and skeletal. The visceral muscles surround the organs. Visceral muscles surrounding the gut can force food to move through the gut. Visceral muscles of the dorsal organ pump hemolymph. The skeletal muscles are responsible for moving the legs, wings, mouthparts, and other appendages of the insect. Insect muscles have many similarities with the muscles of all animals. Muscles evolved early in the evolution of animals and are similar for all animals.

Reproductive System

The reproductive systems of male and female insects each consist of a long tube with two primary branches. The reproductive system has an opening to the outside for sperm (males) or eggs (females). At the other end from the opening are the testes (male) and ovary (female). The male testes produce germ cells called sperm. The female ovaries produce germ cells called oocytes (females). In the ovary, the oocytes and nutrients are packaged in eggs. The eggs develop as they move down the tubes of the reproductive system. The ovaries must pack enough nutrients into each egg for a first-stage larva to complete development.

In males, sperm develop as they pass down the reproductive tract. Many male insects package their sperm in a spermatophore. The spermatophore is a package containing sperm (and often other nutrients) that is delivered to the female during mating. These nutrients can augment the nutrition of the female and allow the pair to produce more or higher quality offspring.

Most insects have internal fertilization. The male copulatory organs fit inside the female copulatory organs and deposit the spermatophore inside the female. The female stores the sperm in a pouch called the spermatheca. When eggs are almost ready to be laid, a sperm from the spermatheca will enter the egg and combine with the oocyte.

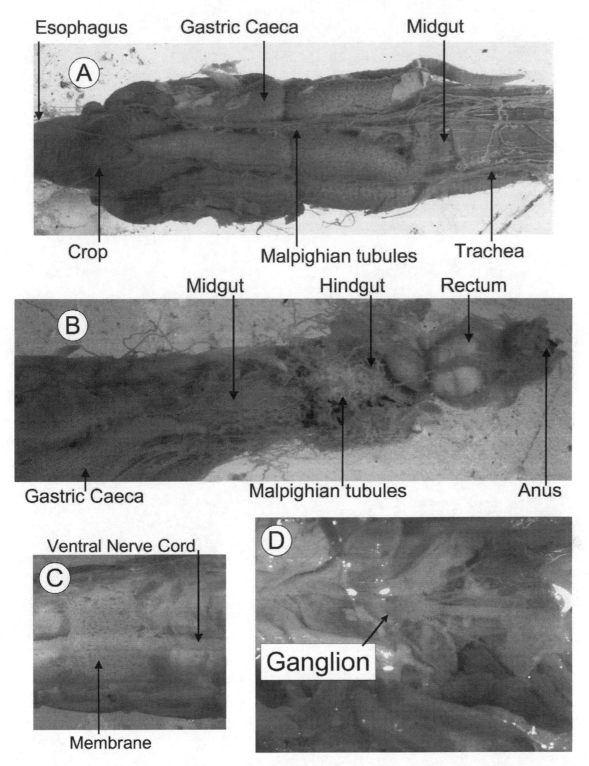

Esophagus   Gastric Caeca   Midgut

A

Crop   Malpighian tubules   Trachea

Midgut   Hindgut   Rectum

B

Gastric Caeca   Malpighian tubules   Anus

Ventral Nerve Cord

C   D

Ganglion

Membrane

A. The anterior of the grasshopper digestive system (removed) from where the esophagous enters the head to midway in the abdomen. B. The posterior of the grasshopper digestive system (removed) from the midway in the abdomen to the anus. C. Top down view of the ventral half of a grasshopper showing the membrane that separates the digestive system (removed) from the ventral nerve chord. Some of the membrane has been removed to expose the ventral nerve chord. D. A thoracic ganglia and major axons leading to the thoracic appendages.

Chapter 4 Study Questions

1. Describe the function of each of the following insect organs:

   A. Salivary glands

   B. Pharynx

   C. Esophagus

   D. Crop

   E. Proventriculus

   F. Gastric Caeca

   G. Midgut

   H. Hindgut

   I. Malpighian tubules

J. Dorsal organ

K. Trachea

L. Tracheole

M. Spiracle

N. Fat Body

O. Spermatheca

2. Does the insect circulatory system transport oxygen?

3. Why do insects have an open circulatory system?

Chapter 5

Insect Locomotion

Terrestrial Locomotion

Walking Legs

Most insects have three pairs of true legs and use all three pairs for walking. The walking legs must support the insect body. Grip is important to small animals such as insects because they have little weight to generate friction. Insect legs often have claws, bristles, spines, or other attachments to improve traction. Cockroaches have backward-facing spines that grip the surface as they run. These spines have a similar function to cleats on the shoes of athletes.

Leg Movement and Gait

Insects may utilize a variety of gaits or pattern of leg movement. A single insect may use different gaits at different speeds. Many walking insects use the alternating triangle gait. In the alternating triangle, the walking insect keeps three legs on the ground and moves the other three. The three that stay on the ground are the front and back legs of one side and the middle leg of the opposite side. Keeping one triangle of legs on the ground while the other triangle moves is a very stable configuration. The alternating triangle in insects has been studied extensively and it is incorporated into the movements of some robots.

Walking cockroaches use the alternating triangle gait. However, running cockroaches may switch to a gallop. During galloping, all legs are off the ground at one time in the gait. In the galloping gait, both hind legs or both forelegs are moved at the same time. Movement alternates between front and hind legs. Alternatively, some insects in a hurry will run on only the hind legs.

Control of Walking

Walking behaviors are hardwired into the insect nervous system. The ganglia of the thorax contain groups of nerves that generate a signal pattern. This signal pattern is sent to the muscles via the motor nerves. The correct signal pattern will coordinate the muscles of the legs to move in the proper sequence such that the insect walks. Because the nerves responsible for walking are located in the thorax, a headless insect may still be able to walk.

Jumping

Insects that jump typically have modified hind legs. Commonly, the leg will have a catch mechanism. The catch mechanism allows the leg muscles to contract without the leg moving. Catch mechanisms operate using the same principle as a catapult. Force is loaded incrementally onto the spring of a catapult. Once released, the spring rapidly unloads all its stored energy and launches the projectile. In jumping insects, force is loaded onto the catch mechanism and the insect itself is the "projectile" that is launched when the energy in the catch mechanism is released.

For example, the hind leg of the grasshopper contains a catch mechanism. When the extensor muscle of the hind leg starts to contract, the leg does not move. The leg is held in place by a catch mechanism. As the muscle continues to contract, the force on the catch mechanism increases. After the catch mechanism is fully loaded, it releases and the leg extends.

The catch mechanism allows muscles to load force. Once the catch mechanism is fully loaded, it releases suddenly. The sudden release delivers more power and speed to the leg than the muscles alone can generate. Catch mechanisms are necessary because muscles contract with either speed or power, but not both. (You can demonstrate this by trying to run while carrying a heavy weight. You will run more slowly with the weight because your leg muscles cannot deliver the same speed with the increased demand for power.)

The joints of insects contain resilin, the most elastic protein known. Resilin is capable of efficient power loading and transfer of power to the leg movement. When muscles contract they compress the resilin in the joint. At the launch point, the joint is finally able to complete its full movement. The resilin "springs back" and the energy released is transferred to the leg movement.

Jumping insects that have hind legs with catch mechanisms include grasshoppers, fleas and spittle bugs (froghoppers). Fleas can jump up to 150 times their length (less than 1 foot) and some froghoppers can jump 400 times their length. (Large animals typically cannot jump very high compared to body length. Why is this good?)

Some insects jump using appendages other than legs. Springtails (Snow Fleas) have a catapult-like device on the end of their abdomen (tail) and a catch mechanism that will spring them into the air.

Click beetles have a peg and catch mechanism between their abdomen and thorax that can propel them into the air if they are lying on their back. Both springtails and click beetles rely on click mechanisms.

Crawling

Crawling is movement in which the body drags on the ground. Some insects, especially the immature stages crawl. Most caterpillars will crawl by first planting their head and contracting their segments, then planting the hindmost segment and pushing the rest of the body forward. Some caterpillars (called inchworms or loopers) will move by moving the hind segment forward toward the head and making a vertical loop with middle of the body. The hind segment is planted and the head and middle of the body can be extended forward. Caterpillars have three pairs of true legs, but they are all on the thorax near the head. Most caterpillars have extensions of the abdomen (prolegs) that support the abdomen or grasp surfaces.

The larvae of some flies are maggots that lack legs altogether. Maggots have spines for traction. Maggots typically crawl using movements similar to those used by caterpillars.

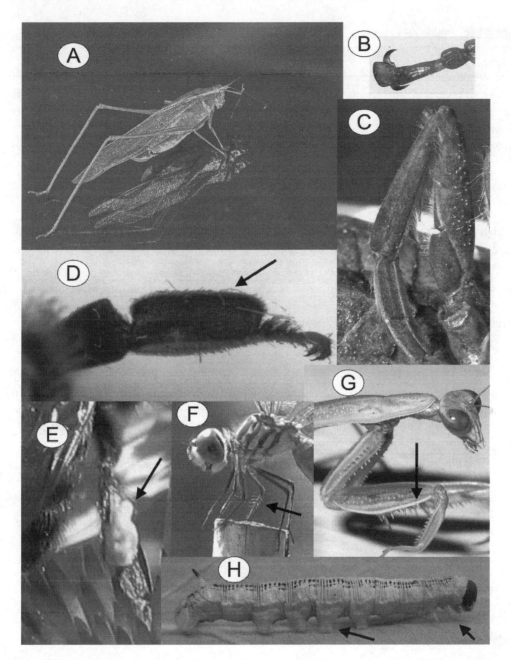

A. Legs separate katydid from the hot surface. Legs have an important role in temperature regulation. B. Claw on the end of a grasshopper leg. Insects use claws for traction the same way that athletes use cleats. C. Swimming hairs on the leg of an aquatic beetle. The hairs stand up (maximum resistance) on the fore stroke and fold down (minimum resistance) on the return stroke. D. Hind legs of bees are modified into a "pollen basket" (arrow) for collecting pollen. E. Bumblebee with pollen baskets (arrow) filled with pollen. F. Legs of dragonflies have spines to aid in catching prey. The leg spines form a basket and can impale small insects. G. Forelegs of the praying mantis are modified for capture of prey. The prey is grasped in the hinge of the leg and impaled on the spines to prevent escape. Legs have taste receptors between the spine to "taste" the prey. H. Caterpillars have six legs (right arrow) on thorax. However the smaller thorax (compared to the abdomen) is not well positioned to support the caterpillar abdomen. Caterpillars have protuberances of the abdomen called prolegs (left arrow) for support and movement of their large abdomen.

Aquatic movement

Aquatic insects may walk on the bottom of a lake or stream, swim through the water, or even walk on top of the water. Water striders are insects that walk on water. The legs of the water striders have special hairs that repel water. These hairs create a meniscus or depression in the water. The insects can push with their legs against the water in a rowing motion to quickly move across the water. The water has surface tension that is large enough to support the weight of the insect and keep it from sinking.

Underwater Movement

Insects that swim underwater often have flat, tapered bodies that are shaped for efficient movement. Legs of swimming or rowing insects may have moveable hairs to help them row. The leg hairs are in sockets so the hairs stand upright if moved in one direction but lay down when moved in the other direction. During the fore stroke, the hairs stand up and push against the water propelling the insect forward. During the return stroke, the hairs fold down allowing the leg to return to its starting position without moving as much water. This adaptation is more efficient for moving through the water than an eliptical rowing motion.

Undulation

Mosquito larvae live in water, but are not good swimmers. They make wiggling movements of their body (undulations) to propel them through the water. Mosquito larvae are sometimes called "wigglers."

Hydrolic Movement

Larvae of dragonflies typically walk on the bottom of a lake or stream. However, when disturbed, they have an escape mechanism that allows them to rapidly shoot through the water. The rectum of the dragonfly is used for oxygen exchange. There are muscles that pump water in and out for more efficient gas exchange. If the muscles rapidly contract, a stream of water will be forced out the posterior of the dragonfly causing it to rapidly shoot forward in the water.

Insect Flight

Origin

No one knows how flight in insects originated. We know that the first land plants appear in the fossil record from 425 million years ago (mya). The oldest insect fossil (about 405 mya) is part of a group known to have wings. Insects were successful and had advantages over other groups of small animals because they had powered flight. Flight helped insects consolidate their position as the most numerous group of animals.

Airborne Transport

Typically, we think of flying animals having wings. However, many small organisms that lack wings are capable of being transported by air without powered flight. Aerobiologists, who study living organisms that are moving through the air, find many interesting little animals without wings. Spiders can spin silk "parachutes" or "balloons" that can catch the wind and allow dispersal. Mites (small arachnids) are commonly found in the air stream. Wingless insects including tiny caterpillars, aphids, and small beetle larvae have been found in the air stream. Wingless animals have little control over take off and landing, but enough individuals land in a suitable habitat that there is advantage to this means of travel.

Evolution of Flight

It is quite possible that flight evolved in tiny insects dispersing by airborne transport. Slight modifications of the thorax to produce lateral flaps would have given greater stability in flight and greater control over landing. Being able to move the flaps would have given even more control over landing. The development of a flap that was moved by a muscle could evolve into a wing through incremental steps. Very tiny insects need very little power to stay aloft. Even today, many of the insects with powered flight are not strong fliers. Once wings and powered flight had evolved, those groups of animals that possessed flight quickly diversified and established.

Flight Efficiency and Small Animals

In the ocean, small animals can move by riding on the ocean currents that are moving above the stationary land at the bottom of the ocean. Once marine animals moved onto land, their movements were more limited and localized. Similar movement for small terrestrial animals would require that the terrestrial animals travel with the atmospheric currents that are moving above the stationary land. Powered flight gives small terrestrial animals the full advantage of atmospheric currents for movement the way ocean currents move small marine animals.

For small terrestrial animals, flight is a much more efficient means of travel than walking. How long would it take a worker ant to walk 100 meters? How long would it take a reproductive ant to fly the same 100 meters? Flying allows insects to traverse much greater distances in less time and less use of energy.

In the terrestrial environment, powered flight gives insects great competitive advantage over groups of animals that lack powered flight. This is an important reason why insects are the most numerous and successful of the terrestrial animals. Insects are notably less successful in the marine environment. Powered flight is a huge advantage for small terrestrial animals, but gives little or no advantage to marine animals that can swim and travel in the water.

How Do Insect Wings Beat?

Most insects move their wings by moving the thorax up and down. The wings are an extension of the thorax and are attached by resilin joints. The sides of the insect thorax act as a fulcrum with the wings and top of the thorax as the lever. When the top of the thorax moves upward, the wings beat down. When the top of the thorax moves down, the wings move up. This is similar to the way a seesaw (found on many playgrounds) operates. You can think of the side of thorax being analogous to the bar that supports the seesaw (fulcrum) and one end of the seesaw being the tip of the wing and the other end being the top of the thorax. As one end of the seesaw goes down (think of the top of the thorax) the other end of the seesaw goes up (think of the tip of the wing).

The thorax forms a box that has elastic properties. There are two opposing sets of flight muscles. One set runs from top to bottom, the other set runs from front to back. By contracting the muscles that run top to bottom, the top of the thorax moves down. The wings are levered up by the sides of the thorax. Contracting the muscles that run front to back forces the top of the thorax up and the sides of the thorax inward. This levers the wings down.

There are two stable wing positions, up and down. The resilin joints of the thorax contain a click mechanism that allows the wings to move with greater power and speed. Muscles can load the click mechanism until it releases. The click mechanism stores power. When the click mechanism releases, it will allow the wings to move faster than the muscles alone could move them. In many insects, the thorax has a natural rate of vibration that may create well over 500 wing beats every second.

Power for Flight

Because insects are so small, the power required to keep them aloft is much less than the power they can generate. The excess power can be used for maneuver, hovering, and other acrobatic activities not seen in larger flying animals.

Bumblebees Can't Fly

In the 1930s, French entomologists analyzed bumble bees and determined that bees could not fly by the aerodynamic principles that govern fixed-winged aircraft. This was mistranslated and misconstrued in the popular press to "Scientists prove that bumble bees can't fly." The contradiction is obvious (bumble bees do indeed fly). A better headline would have been, "Scientists prove that bumble bees can't fly like fixed-winged aircraft." Fixed-wing airplanes generate lift by using air passing over the wings to create lift. Lift is only created when the airplane is moving forward through the air. An airplane that is not moving forward (or moving forward at too slow of speed) will not generate enough lift and stall (or fall out of the sky). The French analysis concluded that insects could not generate enough lift from their wings simply by moving forward through the air at commonly observed speeds.

However, insects don't have fixed wings. Insects generate lift by "paddling" their wings through the air. People (and dogs) can stay afloat in water by "dog-paddling" the water with arms and legs. Many insects "paddle" the air a manner similar to the way we paddle in water. The insect wing does not just move up and down. The insect can adjust its wing attitude during the stroke by muscles directly connected to the wing articulation. Thus, insects do not need to move forward to generate lift with their wings. This allows insects to hover.

Insect wings are capable of generating lift by a variety of mechanisms. (Consider the numerous arm and leg movements that will keep a person afloat in the water.) Bees and flies buzz. Butterflies hang glide. Butterflies flap their wings to generate lift and forward movement, but they can also use their wings like a kite to ride thermals and glide. Large beetles have a clumsy, inelegant flight.

Flying Acrobats

The most acrobatic insect flyers are capable of flying backward as well as forward, hovering or yawing in midair while hovering. Flying insects can multitask including collecting nectar mid-flight and even mating in the air. For the most part, insects do not "roll." Insects use ocelli and gravity detectors to keep their wings parallel to the ground.

How Do Insects Start Flying?

To start flying, insects jump into air. Scientists who study flight can tether insects by attaching a small string to the thorax with a drop of wax. If the feet contact a surface, the wings will stop beating. If the surface is removed, the wings will start beating. In this way we can ask, "How long can insects fly?" Locusts can fly for up to 9 hours. Fruit flies can fly up to 6.5 hours.

Chapter 5 • Insect Locomotion

How Fast Do Insect Wings Beat?

Smaller animals must beat their wings faster than larger animals. Some insect wing beat frequencies are:

Mosquito 300-500 bps (beats per second)
Honeybee 250 bps
Housefly 190 bps
Beetle 50 bps
Butterfly 4-20 bps

Insects with rapid wingbeat frequencies have higher pitched wing sounds. Large insects such as large beetles have a lower pitched wingbeat sound.

Two Wings or Four Wings?

Flying is easier to coordinate with two wings than four wings. Wing beats can create air turbulence that reduces efficiency. If front and hind wings are not coordinated, the hind wings will encounter air turbulence created by the front wings. Most insects either use two wings to fly or have a mechanism to couple the fore and hind wings so they beat in unison. Beetles fly using only two wings. Beetles hold the forewings up and beat only with the hind wings. Butterflies and bees both use all four wings but have physical mechanisms to couple the wings. True flies have only two forewings that are used for flight. The hind wings of flies are modified into knob-like structures (halteres). The halteres generate gyroscopic movements that provide flight stability.

How Fast Do Insects Fly?

The top speed for insect powered flight is a hawk moth measured at 33 mph. Honeybees can fly up to 8 mph and the housefly is capable of 5 mph. Vertebrate predators are capable of much faster speeds than insects. However, many insects can change direction more quickly than their enemies and use their maneuverability to escape predators.

Factors Favoring Flight

Insects gain numerous advantages by being able to fly. For animals of small size, flying is necessary for energy economy. Moving long distances is too inefficient for small animals that rely on walking. Small soil insects and other soil animals that rely on walking typically move very little in their lifetime. Small animals that do not fly are either restricted to tiny areas of a stable resource or concentrate on resources that are widely available in a large contiguous area.

Flight allows insects to leave their food site. Flying insects can feed and develop on small amounts of widely dispersed resources. An insect that depletes the resources in one area can fly to another area. Flight allows insects to exploit patchy (small amounts of a resource that are in scattered locations) resources.

Flying enables insects to find mates even if sparsely distributed in a large territory. Flight allows insects as larvae to be at very low densities, yet traverse enough area as adults to find mates.

Flight makes migration possible. If food becomes scarce, insects can fly to locate a new source of food. Insects such as the Monarch butterfly can move north during the summer to find more food and escape predators and diseases. Monarchs could not migrate if they had to walk instead of fly.

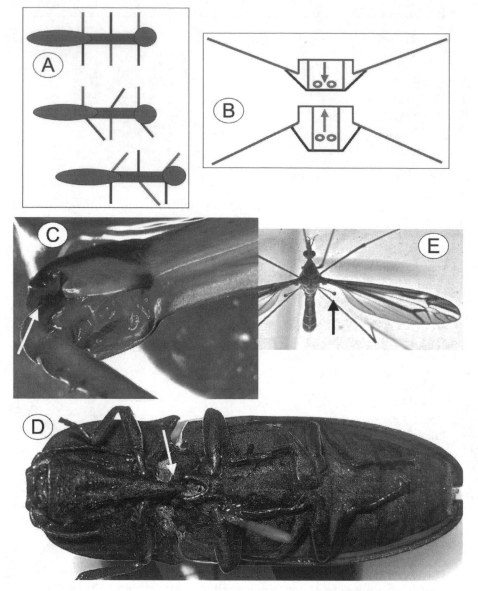

A. The alternating triangle gait offers stability. 3 legs remain on the ground in the shape of a triangle while the other 3 move as shown in the figure. This gait is used in robotics.   B. Most insects beat their wings by moving the top of the thorax (notum) up and down. The notum is pulled down by the tergal-sternal muscles (green) causing the wings to lever up. The dorsal-longitudinal muscles (red) compress the thorax and push the notum upward generating the downward wing beat. The wing joints contain resilin and will rapidly vibrate the wings up and down at a natural frequency. In some cases, this can be 1000 wing beats per second.   C. Insects use click mechanisms to generate movements with both power and speed. The hind leg joint of the grasshopper contains a click mechanism (arrow) that helps the grasshopper jump. The muscles contract and load force on the click mechanism that prevents the leg from moving. At maximum force, the click mechanism gives way and the leg extends with both speed and power. This allows insects to jump large distances relative to their size.   D. The click mechanism (white arrow) of the click beetle is used to right itself. The peg fits in the groove. The insect arches its back and loads force onto the peg. When the peg releases, the force propels the click beetle into the air (with a click) and it turns in the air.   E. The hind wings of flies are modified into knob-like structures called halteres (arrow). Halteres vibrate and generate gyroscopic forces that help the fly turn in the air.

Chapter 5 Study Questions

1. What leg modifications do insects have to improve traction?

2. What is the primary advantage of the alternating triangle gait?

3. Where are the ganglia that control walking located?

4. What features do insects have that improve jumping?

5. Why is flight important to small terrestrial animals like insects?

6. How do movements of the thorax cause the wings to beat up and down?

7. Why is resilin important for insect locomotion?

8. What factors favor the evolution of flight in insects?

9. What mechanisms do insects have to minimize turbulence created by two pairs of wings?

10. What is the relationship between the wingbeat frequency of an insect and the sound it makes when flying?

Chapter 6

Insect Mating and Reproduction

Insect Mating

Why Do Insects and Other Animals Mate?

Mating allows for exchange and recombination of genes. Early in the history of living organisms, those that had the ability to exchange genetic material were more successful than organisms that had no means of genetic exchange. Mating is advantageous for distributing useful gene mutations in a population.

Imagine two individuals, A and B. Individual A has a useful but rare gene mutation, A_m. Individual B has a separate useful but rare gene mutation, B_m. Because A_m and B_m are useful mutations, their frequency will increase in the population. Mating between A_m and B_m individuals will produce individuals with both Mutation A_m and Mutation B_m.

If mating and exchange of genetic traits did not occur, individuals containing both Mutation A_m and Mutation B_m could eventually be produced by a double mutation. However, that would be an extremely rare occurrence and might never happen. Evolution and adaptation to a changing environment can occur much faster for organisms that have sex than ones that do not.

Is Mating Necessary?

No. A few insect species reproduce without ever mating, a process called parthenogenesis. Many species of aphids have an asexual reproductive phase. Asexual female aphids produce offspring that are clones of themselves without mating. However, aphids also have a sexual reproductive phase in which both males and females are produced and mating occurs. Mating is not a requirement for reproduction. However, the fact that the overwhelming majority of animals mate is evidence of its importance.

Roles of Male and Female Insects

Having males and females of a species allows each sex to specialize for different reproductive tasks. Females are specialized for producing eggs. Depending on the species, males may be adapted to a variety of tasks including gathering nutrition, defending resources, or finding mates.

How Do Insects Mate?

Mating in most insects involves internal fertilization similar to mating in mammals. Most insects have reproductive structures located at the end of the abdomen for the transfer of sperm. Males have a retractable abdominal appendage, the aedeagus. The female has a genital opening that is capable of accommodating the male aedeagus.

What Are the Steps in the Insect Mating Process?

Internal fertilization requires a male and a female of the same species to arrive at the same time in the same place in a state capable of mating. Successful mating requires insects to correctly perform a series of complex behaviors that we can divide into mate finding, courtship, and copulation.

Mate finding. For small animals like insects in a complex environment, the mate finding process can be daunting. Complicating the process are predators looking for clues to locate insect prey. Not only must an insect find a mate, but it must also avoid detection by predators. Insects have evolved numerous solutions that bring the sexes together for mating.

Mate finding can be due to random encounter. However, random encounter is only effective for insects that are numerous or in high density in a habitat. Insects can increase their odds of finding a mate by congregating at a single location, most commonly a food resource. For example, insects that are pests of apples may congregate on apple trees. By coming together at a single location, the search for mates is confined to a smaller area.

However, many insects are present in the environment at relatively low densities and must depend on active communication between males and females. Communication may involve combinations of sound, odor, visual displays, or the production of light.

Male crickets, grasshoppers, and cicadas "sing" to attract females. Most female moths produce odors called pheromones that can attract males from long distances. Male moths have odor receptors on their antennae that are supersensitive only to the pheromone odor of their own females. Most butterflies recognize mates by the visual pattern on their wings. Male and female fireflies use flashes of light to communicate in an insect "Morse Code."

The swarms of gnats we see above our lawn are groups of small male flies advertising their presence. These swarms, called mating leks, contain all males and communicate both visually and chemically to females. The swarms are more visible from a distance than a single male would be. The swarms also produce odors (pheromones) that are attractive to the females. Males in a group are easier to locate because they are more visible and produce a stronger odor than single males.

Courtship

Once males and females are in close proximity, an elaborate courtship ritual may be necessary. Courtship in insects may involve combinations of singing, dancing, odor, touching, or visual cues. Males of predatory insects may need to present the female with a "gift" such as a food item or a nutritional secretion to preoccupy the female. There are a variety of unusual courtship rituals in insects. Only a small fraction of the mating and courtship rituals have been recorded in detail.

During the courtship process, the male and female engage in behaviors that align them in the appropriate position relative to each other to begin copulation. These mating behaviors are innate and often stereotypic. People that study insect mating occasionally observe "aberrant behavior." Insects with "aberrant behavior" typically fail to reproduce.

Copulation

In order for insects to copulate, the male and female must align physically. Mating positions vary among insect groups but are often the same within a group. For example, most beetles mate with the male on top, while most moths mate end to end. The mechanics and behaviors involved in mating are conserved in evolution.

Some insect species have complex genitalia that physically prevent closely related species from mating by "lock and key" mechanisms. In these species, the male aedeagus has a unique shape that only fits the genital opening of females of the same species. The shape prevents mating with females of other species because of physical restrictions. Taxonomists often use the reproductive structures of the male and female to correctly identify the species.

Unusual Sperm Transfer Mechanisms

Some insects use mechanisms that involve structures other than the typical reproductive appendages at the end of the abdomen. Other insects dispense with internal fertilization altogether, engaging instead in external fertilization.

Damselfly and dragonfly males deposit sperm in a pouch near the front of their abdomen. Prior to mating, the males bend the tip of the abdomen to deposit the sperm in the pouch. During mating, the males use the end of their abdomen to grasp the female between the head and thorax. The female uses the reproductive structure at the end of her abdomen to collect sperm from his pouch by bending her abdomen. This behavior is called a mating wheel. During egg laying, the male and female of some species fly in tandem with the male grasping the female behind the head. When the eggs are laid in the water, the male can provide extra lift to pull the female out of the water.

Bed bug females have a special plate on the anterior of the abdomen that is used for mating. Males perforate the cuticle through the plate and deposit sperm directly into hemocoel. Bed bug males transfer nutrients and sperm. The sperm must travel through the hemolymph to reach the eggs in the female ovary.

Honey bee males have detachable genitalia. Queen bees mate multiple times in flight. A male and a female flying together would be aerodynamically unsound. Once copulation has occurred, the male honeybee does a back flip, and falls to the ground. His genitalia detach and remain in the Queen. The genitalia have muscles that pump the sperm into the queen even after it detaches from the male. The male bee, having successfully mated, dies soon afterward.

External Sperm Transfer

Some groups of insects can exchange genes without direct contact between males and females in a process called external sperm transfer. An example of an insect with external sperm transfer is the silverfish, a tiny wingless insect. (Some species of silverfish are not uncommon in old houses in areas with damp wood.) In most species of silverfish, the male silverfish spins a silk thread and attaches sperm and nutrients to the thread. A female silverfish that walks under the thread and contacts the sperm will be inseminated.

External Fertilization, with "Ritual"

Some species of silverfish use a more elaborate ritual. In these species, the male first maneuvers the female to the sperm, then uses the silk thread to tie up the female. The female is released only after insemination. This process requires more complex behaviors, but utilizes male resources more effectively.

Why Is Internal Fertilization More Common Than External Fertilization?

Internal fertilization provides protection for the sperm. Internal fertilization allows males to make fewer sperm and concentrate their resources. Males using internal fertilization can make a greater contribution to offspring by transferring nutrients to the female in addition to the sperm. Each sperm produced by a male has a greater probability of success with internal fertilization compared with external fertilization.

Problems with external sperm transfer include lack of protection of sperm from predators and a low probability of a sperm finding an egg. External fertilization limits the contribution that a male can make to a female during reproduction. In insects with external fertilization, males may consume the sperm of competing males. Consuming the sperm both removes some of the competition and allows the male to use the nutrients of its rivals to make more of its own sperm. Sperm predation selects against males that provision the sperm with excess nutrients.

What Substances Are Transferred During Mating?

Insects with internal fertilization commonly transfer substances during mating in addition to sperm. These substances include nutrients, hormones, and defensive chemicals.

Nutrients. Cockroaches have a diet that is very low in nitrogen. Male cockroaches accumulate nitrogen in the form of uric acid. During mating, the males transfer uric acid to the female. The female is capable of processing the uric acid and uses it to make amino acids and proteins for provisioning the eggs. The contribution of uric acid by the male increases the number of eggs produced.

Defensive chemicals. Some moths sequester toxins from plants as caterpillars. The male moths will transfer their toxins to the female during mating. Females add the toxins to their eggs to protect them from predators such as ants. The contribution of defensive chemicals by the male makes the egg better defended.

Can Insects Choose Their Mate?

Yes. The choice of a mate is important. Good mates produce more progeny (female) or allow the production of more progeny (male). Good mates help produce progeny with better survival. There are a variety of ways that insects can assess mate quality. Size is often an indication of the ability to deliver nutrients and some insects will respond more readily to potential mates that are larger or have larger features. An example is the stalk eyed fly. The largest males have eyes that are the greatest distance apart. Males of larger size win territory and females.

The amount of a chemical produced can indicate the quality of the mate. For example, in some male moths that provide females with defensive chemicals during mating, some of the toxin is also used to produce a male pheromone (scent). Females can judge the quality of the male (amount of toxin the male can contribute to the eggs) by the strength of the odor.

Some insects use nuptial gifts. The male presents the female with a prey item. The female assesses the gift as a measure of male quality. Better males give better gifts and produce more offspring. Nuptial gifts are not uncommon among predators. For the male, a nuptial gift can occupy the female during mating and the getaway, so the male doesn't become dinner.

In the dance flies, the primitive behavior of giving a prey item as a nuptial gift has evolved into a complex non-food present. The preference of females for larger prey gave an advantage to males that wrapped silk around smaller prey items to make them appear larger. Wrapping the prey has the added advantage of occupying the female for a longer period and allowing more time for insemination. The female must first unwrap the gift prior to feeding, thus lengthening the time the male has to mate. In some flies, the gift has evolved to be a fancy silk wrapping that contains no prey item at all!

Mate Guarding

Males that invest substantial nutrients in a female may engage in mate guarding. After mating, the male stays with the female to prevent other males from mating with her. Other forms of mate guarding do not require the male to be present. Some male crickets will seal the female genitalia with a plug to prevent other males from mating (a cricket chastity belt). Male moths can prevent mating by using hormones. Male moths commonly transfer a hormone along with their sperm. The hormone ends pheromone production so the female will not attract other males. Fruit flies have a toxin in their semen. Although females can mate multiple times, females that mate too many times will die from the toxin.

Do Insects Have Gay Genes?

The fruit fly is an important insect for studying the effect of genes on behavior. A gene that is important in male mating behavior is the *fruitless* (Drosophila) gene.

Wild-type male fruit flies have a genetically based courtship ritual. The male orients toward and follows the female, taps her with his forelegs, sings a species-specific courtship song by extending and vibrating one wing and curls his abdomen to attempt copulation. Unreceptive females will reject the male by moving away. The receptive female fruit fly produces a chemical aphrodisiac pheromone that attracts the male. Receptive females will remain and mate with the male.

The *fruitless* mutant affects the central nervous system of the male fruit fly. This leads to aberrant mating behavior and rejection by females. The males indiscriminately court both females and other males. If *fruitless* males are isolated from females, they will form long mating chains of males trying to copulate with each other.
This is clear evidence of genes affecting sexual orientation in fruit flies. This is not at all surprising because there is a strong genetic component attached to reproductive behaviors. There is increasing evidence for a genetic component to sexual orientation in humans. Studies of the genetics and mechanisms of sexual orientation in insects can provide clues for the study of sexual orientation in humans.

An important caveat is, "Humans are not fruit flies." Human behavior occurs in a more complex social environment. Fruit flies are not social and their behaviors may not always translate to humans. Nonetheless, studies of the genetics of insect behavior, including sexual behaviors can lead to a better understanding of the genetics of some human behaviors.

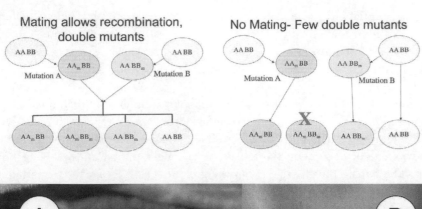

Mating allows recombination, double mutants

No Mating- Few double mutants

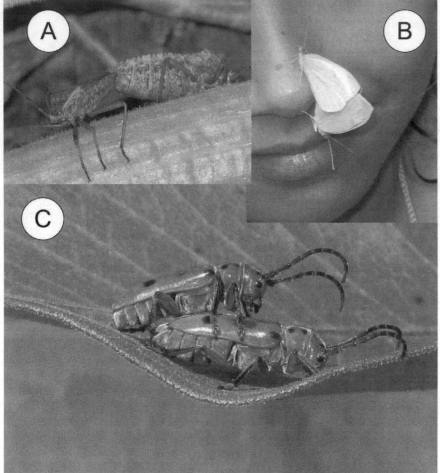

Diagrams. Left: Mating allows for exchange of genes. An individual with mutation A could mate with an individual with mutation B and produce individuals with any combination- original type, A only, B only or double mutant. Right: In the absence of mating, double mutant (A B) cannot be produced unless there is a new mutation event. If mutations are rare, then double mutants would be created more rapidly in an organism sex than in an organism lacking sex.

A. Squash bugs mate end to end. The egg-producing female (right) is larger than the male. Mating positions are typically conserved within related groups because sexual behaviors are under intense selection pressure. Most Paraneoptera mate end to end as do Lepidoptera.   B. Captured cabbage white butterflies continue mating oblivious to their surroundings. Most butterflies mate in the air and land to rest.   C. A milkweed beetle pair with the male on top, the mating position of most beetles. The male on top position is also used by the mantids, the Diptera and the Orthoptera.

Chapter 6 • Insect Mating and Reproduction

Chapter 6 Study Questions

1. What advantage does mating give living organisms?

2. What three steps must occur for insects to mate by direct copulation?

3. What is unique about sperm transfer in dragonflies?

4. What is unique about sperm transfer in bed bugs?

5. What group of insects uses external fertilization?

6. What are some advantages of internal fertilization compared to external fertilization?

7. In addition to sperm, what substances do insects transfer during mating?

8. Why is mate guarding common in insects with males that deliver substantial nutrients to the female?

9. What is a nuptial gift and why are they important?

10. What gene affects mate preference in fruit flies?

Chapter 7

Insect Senses: Taste, Odor, Sound, and Vision

Insect Taste Receptors

What Are Receptors?

Receptors are cells that are specialized for detecting signals present in the environment. Receptors may be specialized to detect chemicals, temperature, light, movement, sound, or other features of the environment. The information gathered by receptors is converted into bioelectrical signals and transmitted by neurons to the central nervous system where the information is processed.

What Are Taste Receptors?

Taste receptors are cells that are responsive to chemicals in the environment. In humans, taste receptors are distinguished from olfactory receptors by their location. Human taste receptors are present in the mouth and provide information about chemicals in food or other substances that enter the mouth. Human olfactory receptors are located in the nose and respond to volatile chemicals that enter the nose. Both olfactory and taste receptors respond to chemical stimuli.

Insect taste receptors are defined as receptors that must directly contact chemicals in solution as compared to olfactory receptors that are capable of detecting airborne chemicals. Both taste and olfactory receptors have similar mechanisms for response to chemicals and the distinct separation of insect taste and odor is blurry. For insects, it is perhaps more useful to think in terms of arrays of chemical receptors with their output being integrated in local ganglia. The primary olfactory center is the olfactory lobe of the insect brain that processes information from the antenna. The primary taste center is the subesophageal ganglia, which integrates information from receptors on the mouthparts. Additional receptors that detect chemicals in the environment are found in a variety of other locations including the ends of the legs and the tip of the ovipositor (egg-laying organ of female insects).

What Can Insects Taste?

Insects can taste **sweet**, **sour**, **bitter**, and **salt**. Insect taste is not exactly the same as human taste. To us, diet cola containing aspartame (NutraSweet) tastes sweet. Hungry flies will drink cola containing sugar. Hungry flies will not drink diet cola. Diet cola does not taste "sweet" to flies. The taste receptors of flies must be different from human "sweet" receptors because artificial sweeteners do not taste sweet to flies but they do to us.

How Do Taste Receptors Work?

The membranes of taste receptors contain proteins that interact with some chemicals but not others. Taste receptors for "sweet" have proteins in their membrane that respond to sugar but lack proteins that respond to salt. Taste receptors for "salt" have proteins in their membrane that respond to sodium but lack proteins that respond to sugar. The type of protein the receptor cell makes will determine what type of receptor (sweet, salt, sour, bitter) it is. When a receptor responds to a chemical, it sends an electrical signal to the nervous system.

Where are Insect Taste Receptors Located?

Human taste receptors are found only in our mouth. In contrast, insects have taste receptors on many parts of their body. Insect taste receptors are located on body parts that directly contact food or the environment. Taste receptors are located on the mouthparts, end of the legs, and ovipositor.

Why Do Insects Have Taste Receptors on the Feet?

Most insects have taste receptors on their tarsi or "feet." The fly walking across a surface with droplets of sugar can taste the sugar without lowering its mouthparts or feeding! Being able to taste with the feet allows the insect to sample the surface continuously without having to stop and lower its mouthparts. This is especially important for insects that make a meal out of very small bits of food spread over a large area. Taste receptors on the feet make the food easier to locate. Considering some of the substances that insects land upon (manure for instance) tasting with the feet can reduce exposure to pathogens compared to lowering the mouthparts onto these substances.

Why Do Butterflies Tap?

Some insects, such as butterflies, have claws on their feet and release plant juices by tapping on the leaves. The plant juices contain different chemicals (and therefore different information) than a leaf surface. Chemicals on a dry surface must first dissolve in water before they can be detected. Tapping allows the butterfly to get more information about leaf taste with its feet.

How Does a Praying Mantis Taste Its Prey?

The preying mantis captures prey with its legs. Mantis legs have large spines that impale the prey and prevent its escape. Liquid oozes from the impaled prey. Some of the oozing liquid contacts taste receptors between the leg spines of the mantis. The mantis can "taste" the impaled prey with its raptorial legs before it touches the mouth. The mantis can decide if the prey is edible before it starts to eat.

How Do Insects Know Where to Lay Eggs?

Female insects often have taste receptors on the ovipositor (egg-laying organ) on the end of the abdomen. The receptors on the ovipositor will taste the surface where the egg is to be laid. The ovipositor taste receptors tell the insect if it is laying an egg on a good food for the larva.

What Do Taste Receptors Look Like?

Taste receptor cells are located in the layer of epidermal cells that secrete the cuticle. Taste receptor cells have processes that extend to the surface of the insect cuticle and are most often pegs, pits, or hairs. The hairs or pits have tiny pores that allow chemicals to enter, dissolve in a fluid, and contact the membrane of the taste receptor.

How Do Insects Decide to Feed?

Taste receptors provide insects with information about a potential meal. Sugars give plants a sweet taste. However, most plants are not edible because they produce toxins. Some plants (such as deadly nightshade) can kill people or pets if eaten. The same toxins can kill insects if consumed. Toxins typically have a bitter taste. Taste receptors give information about the relative concentrations of bitter and sweet. This information is used to assess the toxin to nutrient ratio of the food.

Many studies on insect decisions to feed have used blow flies. Blow flies are easy to rear in colonies. Adults are relatively easy to manipulate. Adult blow flies will lower their mouthparts if their taste receptors are stimulated by sugar. Thus it is easy to determine when a blow fly decides to feed.

From these experiments we know that hungry flies are less choosy than flies that are satiated. A starved fly will readily consume a very weak solution of sugar in water. A fly that is less starved requires a higher concentration of sugar before it will feed.

Bitter substances may deter a fly from feeding on weak sugar solution. In the presence of a bitter substance the concentration of sugar needed to stimulate a fly to feed is higher. However, insects that are hungry enough will eat very bitter substances.

How do you decide what you eat? Does being very hungry change what you are willing to eat? Hunger is a primitive sensation and feeding is a primitive behavior that may have commonalities in most animals.

Other Insect Senses

How Do Insects Detect Temperature?

Insects can detect temperature and humidity although specific organs and receptors have not been identified. Most nerve cells will respond to change in temperature with a change in the signal pattern. Insects may sense temperature by changes in activity in nerves that are not highly specialized. Some insects can discriminate as little as two degrees difference in temperature.

How Do Insects Detect Humidity?

Insects can detect humidity differences, but the receptors for humidity detection have not been identified. Humans can also sense differences in humidity but the mechanism is not entirely clear. High humidity reduces the rate of evaporation from the surface and may be detected secondarily as an affect on surface temperature. In humans, high humidity affects the ability of the lungs to exhale water vapor. In insects, the spiracles of the respiratory system remain open longer under high humidity than under low humidity.

How Do Insects Detect Gravity?

Some insects can detect gravity by the downward pull on parts of the body. In some insects, hairs between the head and the thorax are able to measure the downward pull of gravity on the head. Bees can be tricked into flying erratically by attaching a small weight to their head. The weight changes the angle between the head and the thorax. The bee will change its flight attitude until the proper spacing between the head and thorax is achieved.

Many aquatic insects have internal organs that are pulled downward by the force of gravity. These organs may incorporate metal ions that give them a high density. The organs are connected to receptors that are stretched when the insect is upside down and the gravity detection organ is pulled toward the top of the insect. The receptors are relaxed when the insect is upright and the gravity detection organ is pulled toward the bottom of the insect

Some terrestrial insects seem to have little sense of gravity. Many plant-feeding insects are equally comfortable walking on the upper or lower side of a plant leaf. Because of their small size, gravity has less of an effect on them that it would on a larger animal.

Do Insects Get Dizzy?

Humans have an inner ear organ that senses change in motion. Activities that cause the fluid in the organ to suddenly move can create a sensation of "dizziness." Since insects lack an inner ear organ, there is no indication that insect get dizzy or airsick.

Odors and Insects

How Do Insects Use Odors?

Insects may use odors to find food, mates, egg-laying sites, and other resources.

What are Odors?

Odors are caused by airborne chemicals. Airborne chemicals are perceived as odors if they contact odor receptors that respond to those chemicals.

What Produces Odors?

Any process that releases chemicals into the air can produce an odor. Some odors come from abiotic (non-living) processes. Most odors (airborne chemicals) result from biological processes. Living organisms produce chemicals through routine processes. These chemicals can volatize into the air and become odors.

Routine odors are often used by insects to find resources. Mammals release carbon dioxide during breathing and lactic acid in sweat. Carbon dioxide and lactic acid may be used by mosquitoes and other biting flies to locate a host. Dead animals release characteristic odors that are attractive to saprophagic insects. Manure odors attract flies dung beetles and other coprophagic insects.

Why Do Plants Produce Odors?

Plants that are pollinated by insects produce attractive odors. Flowers that attract bees often have a sweet smell. A side benefit of flowers attracting bee pollinators is that flowers smell good to us.

Flowers that are pollinated by flies, such as skunk cabbages, often smell bad to us. Plants that are pollinated by wind do not need to attract insects and may lack a distinctive odor.

How are Odors Used for Communication?

Some of the most important insect odors are produced intentionally for communication. Female moths produce chemicals, called pheromones (an insect perfume) that attract male moths of the same species. Pheromones are often mixtures of chemicals (blends). Each species of moth uses a unique pheromone blend. Moth species can be differentiated by the pheromone blend alone.

How are Odors Used for Defense?

Foul odors may deter potential predators. For example, stink bugs release foul smelling chemicals. The "stink" advertises their toxicity. People who pick up stink bugs will have bad smelling fingers for an extended time. For this reason, most people (and many predators) avoid handling stink bugs.

How Do Insects Detect Odors?

The primary odor reception organ in insects is the antenna. (In humans, our odor receptors are inside our nose.) The antenna of insects is comparable to a nose turned inside out.

The insect antenna is an extended platform that can sweep chemicals out of the air. Antennae have a large surface area that can accommodate many odor receptors. As the insect walks or flies, air passes over the antennae. Chemicals in the air dissolve in the antennal fluid. A chemical that produces an odor travels through the antennal fluid and interacts with a protein receptor on the surface of an antennal receptor cell. The receptor cells in the antenna send signals through nerves to the insect brain when an odor is detected. Like taste receptors, odor receptors are selective. Receptors are typically receptive to some chemicals but not others.

What Odors are Detected?

The air is full of chemicals, but not all chemicals can be detected by all species of insects at the concentrations present in the air. The ability to detect an odor depends on the receptors. Insects are only sensitive to some chemicals but not others. Chemicals in the air that do not stimulate odor receptors are "odorless." For example, methane, the gas used in ovens and home heating is odorless to humans. To alert users to potentially dangerous leaks, an odorant that is detected at very low concentrations is added to the gas. Similarly, many chemicals are also odorless to insects.

The ability to detect odors varies widely among insect species. Insects that depend on odors to locate resources important to growth and reproduction typically have well developed systems for detecting those odors. Insects may have many receptors that are finely tuned to detect a single important chemical. These receptors may be responsive to only a single chemical at very low concentrations.

Pheromones. Pheromones are critical to the reproductive success of moths. Males of most species of moths have olfactory systems that are excellent pheromone detectors. Compared to the antenna of the female moth, the male antenna typically has more surface area and a more highly branched structure. The greater surface accommodates more pheromone specific receptors. Most pheromone receptors respond only to pheromones and do not respond to other odors at naturally occurring concentrations. This ability to discriminate allows male moths to concentrate on odors from potential mates and not be confused by odors from other species.

The large numbers of pheromone sensitive receptors allow male moths to detect pheromones in trace amounts. Male moths can use pheromone to find females at distances over 1 km (2/3 mile). However, the pheromone amount is so small that predators seldom detect the female. Humans cannot detect the small amounts of pheromone that insects use.

In contrast to the male, female moths may have few or no receptors that detect their own pheromones and typically do not respond to their own pheromone. In some moths, the female antennae have receptors that are sensitive to odors of plants that are food for their offspring.

Dead animal odor. Female blow flies have many odor receptors that are sensitive to dead animal odors. Dead bodies are rich in nutrients and the first insects to arrive typically produce more offspring. Thus, there is intense favorable selection for those female blow flies with the odor system best able to detect and locate a dead body. Even faint odors are readily detected, sometimes at considerable distance. Blow flies can arrive at within an hour after an animal dies.

Dung odors. Manure is an important resource for many insects especially dung beetles and flies. These insects are able to detect manure odors and arrive at the source of manure to lay eggs. Like dead bodies, manure is rich in nutrients. Those insects that arrive first derive the most benefit. Selection for ability to detect dung odor is keen in dung-feeding insects.

How are Insect Odors Useful to Us?

In some instances we can use our knowledge of odors that are important to insects for their detection and control. Baiting traps with chemicals known to attract insects provides a convenient method for detection and monitoring of insect populations. Attractants may be food odors. However, the most potent attractants are the sex attractant pheromones. Pheromones often only attract a single species of insect. This makes it easy to monitor a specific pest. Pheromone traps can reduce the amount of time needed to monitor populations.

For example, gypsy moth is an invasive species that is spreading across the U.S. primarily by humans moving firewood and camping equipment. Small isolated populations can be controlled if detection occurs early. A grid of gypsy moth pheromone traps has been in place in Indiana for many years to detect the spread. One trap is placed in every square mile of the state. Because gypsy moth males can detect pheromone at very low concentrations and fly relatively long distances, the traps are effective at detecting new populations shortly after they are introduced. If detected, measures are taken to eliminate the gypsy moths.

In addition to monitoring, pheromones may be used for control of some insect pests by mating prevention. Recently pheromones were used to eradicate a population of gypsy moth in Indianapolis. Tiny dispensers containing the pheromone are sprayed onto foliage of trees just before adult female gypsy moths emerge from their pupae. The male moths spend all their time trying to mate with the numerous artificial dispensers and are unable to locate the more rare female gypsy moths. This control method is called mating disruption or the male frustration technique. The mating prevention technique is most effective against low-density populations. At high densities, enough males find a female in spite of the pheromone dispensers to produce the next generation.

Hazards of Pheromones

One of the hazards of working with pheromones is their potent attraction to male moths. People who work with pheromones often have trace amounts on their skin and clothing. When I was working with gypsy moth pheromone during a gypsy moth outbreak in Massachusetts, my car and my apartment filled with gypsy moths. While playing outfield on my softball team, I was accompanied by a cloud of male gypsy moths. They even followed me to a Red Sox baseball game in Fenway Park. The woman sitting in front of me kept swatting at the cloud of gypsy moths and said, "I don't understand it. They all seem to be attracted to me."

How are insect odors discovered? Important odors may be characterized by a combination of behavioral observations and chemical analysis. For instance, a female moth can be placed in a trap. Capturing more males in a trap with a female than a trap without a female may indicate the involvement of a pheromone.

The female can be placed in a device to collect odors. The collected odors can be placed in a dispenser and tested in a trap to see if odor alone can attract males. If males are attracted to odors, then chemists can be enlisted to identify the pheromone.

Antennae of male moths are useful tools in the identification of pheromones. Responses of the antennal receptors can be measured using electrodes. When pheromone contacts the antenna, a strong response is measured. If a chemical that is not a pheromone contacts the antenna no response or only a very weak response is detected.

The odor collected from a female moth may contain both pheromone and other chemicals. Chemists are able to separate the individual chemicals that are released from a female. The individual chemicals that cause the largest response in a male antenna (most likely to be the pheromone) are identified. Chemists then synthesize or isolate the chemicals for testing on male moths. The putative pheromone can be tested for its ability to attract male moths in the wild. If the correct chemical blend has been identified and synthesized, it will mimic the activity of a female moth and attract the male moths.

Pheromones have been identified for hundreds of species of insects by this process. Pheromones are widely used in insect pest management programs, primarily for detecting the presence of pest insects.

Insect Sound

What is sound? Sound is vibration transmitted through gas, liquid, or solid. Acoustics is the study of sound.

Sound Production

Insects sounds can be classified as inadvertent sounds, such as those caused by moving and feeding, and communication sounds that are typically produced by special sound organs.

Insects that make loud sounds usually have a two-part sound organ consisting of a primary sound organ and a resonator. Muscles vibrate the primary sound organ to produce the sound. The vibrations of the primary sound organ cause a larger organ, the resonator, to vibrate and amplify the sound (make it louder). The larger resonator creates sound waves with larger amplitudes. The larger amplitude is easier to detect and travels a longer distance. The receiver detects the larger amplitude as an increase in volume.

Examples of Sound Organs

File and Plectrum

Crickets and katydids use a file (teeth) and plectrum system located on their wings. The wings are asymmetric. One wing contains the file and the opposite contains the plectrum. The file has teeth, like the teeth of the comb. If you bend the teeth of a comb by pushing them across a solid bar (plectrum) the teeth will produce an audible sound as they bend back into place. Thus katydids, crickets, and grasshoppers have a primary sound organ that produces sound the same way a comb does.

Crickets and katydids have a resonator (called a harp) that resides underneath the file and plectrum on the wings. The vibration from the file and plectrum vibrates the air within the harp. The harp directs the sound wave away from the insect in much the same way that a sound stage or a megaphone directs sound.

Grasshoppers have file and plectrum systems located on their body but not confined to the wings. Some grasshoppers have a file (teeth) on the leg that they rub against a wing vein (Plectrum). Other grasshoppers have a file on the hind femur and a plectrum on the abdomen. In grasshoppers the abdomen serves as the resonator that amplifies the sound.

Many insect species can be distinguished by their unique sound. Insects sounds differ in frequency, pattern per bout, and spacing of bouts. Crickets and katydids can make a sound pattern with a single movement of the wings. The pattern of sound is determined by the spacing, size, and number of teeth in file, the pause between wing movements, and the rate of wing movement.

Insect "Drummers"

Some insects including cicadas produce sound by vibrating a membrane called the tympanum. This produces sound in a manner similar to vibrating the head of a drum. The tympanum of the cicada is the primary vibrator and the abdomen is the resonator that amplifies the sound. Cicadas make a variety of calls. Males chorus to attract females. The chorusing changes to a courtship song at close range. Cicadas signal alarm when handled. Periodic cicadas can produce very loud sounds, up to 120 decibels (ear pain level).

In many insects, it is the male that makes the sound. Male insects use sound for a variety of purposes including attracting females and establishing territory. Making sounds can be hazardous because it can attract predators. Many insects call at night as a way of reducing predation. Most insects that make noise will cease if a potential predator approaches.

Insect "Whistlers"

Hissing roaches produce their hissing sound through modified spiracles. Air is forced through the small holes to produce the hiss. The hiss is startling and can cause a predator to drop the roach and allow it to escape.

The honeybee robber is a hawk moth known to rob beehives for honey. When handled, the moth squeaks like a mouse, a noise that calms bees. The sound is thought to mimic the queen. The sound is made by forcing air through the proboscis (mouthparts).

Head Bangers

When termite colonies are under attack, the soldiers communicate with the colony by banging their heads against the tunnel. This creates a vibration that recruits defenders. Many species of ants can "stridulate" or create vibrations that can be transmitted to the surface. Vibrations communicated through a solid surface can be transferred to an insect leg and detected by organs in the insect legs.

Inadvertent Noises

Inadvertent noise is created by most animals and has potential use for detection of insects. Chewing creates ultrasound vibrations that can be detected by appropriate devices. Some wood boring insects can use these chewing sounds to communicate with each other. However, these sounds may also be detected by predators, that use the sounds to locate prey.

The noise produced by the buzzing bee or mosquito is caused by wing movements. These vibrations of female mosquito wings are used in mate recognition by male mosquitoes. The sounds made by each species have distinctive patterns. Recently developed sound detectors can process the sounds and identify insect species on the basis of wing beat sound alone. Such technology may be useful in remote sensors used to detect insects of interest.

Sound Receptors

Humans detect vibrations by hearing or touch. Hearing describes only those vibrations that are detected by the ear. All other vibrations are detected by touch. Insects have multiple mechanisms to detect vibrations but lack ears. Humans and insects can detect some of the same sounds. However, insects detect some sounds humans cannot.

There are a variety of sound detection organs in insects. A tympanum is a common detection device. A tympanum is a membrane like the head of a drum. The diameter and physical qualities of the membrane determine its natural frequency of vibration. Tympanal sound detectors are optimized (or tuned) to detect frequencies important to the insect. "Tuning" the receptor helps filter noise and increases ability to detect signal. Grasshoppers, katydids, and crickets have tympanal sound detection organs that preferentially vibrate in response to sound of the frequency produced by potential mates.

Mosquitoes detect sound with a special organ at the base of the antenna. Male mosquitoes orient to the sounds made by the wings of flying females.

Bat Detectors

Sound detection is highly advanced in some moths. Bats, important predators of night flying moths, navigate by sonar (emitting, then receiving reflected sounds). Some moths have tympanal hearing organs that detect the sounds emitted by bats. In highly developed systems, moths detect bats at 40 meters, while bats can only detect moths at about 5 meters. Moths respond to detection of bat sound by a variety of avoidance maneuvers. This includes erratic flight, or an upward loop followed by a power dive. Bat sounds can be recorded and played back to study the moth response to the recording. Moths will respond to recordings of bats in much the same way they respond to the bat itself.

Trash-Talking Moths

Some moths are unpalatable and not edible by bats. To avoid attack, these moths advertise their distastefulness by emitting noises that the bats can detect. When bat sonar detects one of these moths, the bat sonar signal returns along with the moth sound. Bats avoid these trash-talking moths.

Insect Vision

Visual Systems

The visual systems of animals have basic units called photoreceptors. Each photoreceptor collects light and signals the nervous system. Light detection by a photoreceptor depends on its properties. Photoreceptors differ in sensitivity to wavelength of light (red, green, blue, UV). Each photoreceptor creates a signal output that is based on the total stimulatory effect of all the light that reaches it. A photoreceptor can only provide information and signal the intensity of its stimulation. All other sensations that we associate with vision—images, colors, objects, movement—are created by the brain. The brain receives the signals from all the receptors, then integrates and processes the information to create "vision."

Because vision is a sensation, or product of processing in the brain, we cannot know the visual sensation of other animals (including insects) or even other people. For instance, some people differ in their visual sense (color-blindness, dyslexia, myopia). The visual sense of animals may be very different from ours. We cannot know what other animals see. We can investigate their visual systems to deduce what they are capable of seeing.

Vision in Insects

What kind of eyes do insects have?
Most flying adult insects have compound eyes. Insects may also have simple eyes. Simple eyes include ocelli and stemmata.

What Are Ocelli?

Ocelli are simple eyes that contain one or only a few photoreceptors. Ocelli are only capable of detecting shades of light. Ocelli are not capable of forming complex images because there are not enough receptors. How do insects use ocelli? We cannot know all the uses. Many flying insects have ocelli. The ocelli can provide information on the direction of the light. Information from the ocelli could help keep the insect oriented properly when flying.

Ocelli may also have a role in detecting photoperiod, the relative lengths of the light and dark cycles of a day. In higher latitudes, the length of the daylight is much longer in mid-summer than at the equinox. Insects can determine the season based on the length of the daylight compared to the length of the night. Information from simple light receptors could be integrated to determine day length.

Stemmata

Stemmata are the simple eyes present on caterpillars. The stemmata are typically arranged in a field. Like ocelli, each stemmata is only sensitive to light and dark and cannot produce a complex image. However, the caterpillar brain can integrate changes in light patterns across the stemmata field to detect the movement of a shadow. Caterpillars are capable of detecting and responding to movement with clusters of stemmta on their head.

Compound Eyes

Compound eyes are clusters of many units called ommatidia. A compound eye may contain 10,000 or more ommatidia. Each ommatidia contains several photoreceptors (commonly nine). A single ommatidia senses light and dark and may provide information to create "color." We can think of an insect compound eye as an array of receptors. Each receptor creates a single "pixel" of information that is used by the brain to create a larger pattern. This is similar to the way that pixels on a computer screen in aggregate form a "picture."

Color

In most insects a single ommatidia contains multiple receptors. These receptors differ in wavelength sensitivity. A single ommatidia can produce different versions of the same pixel, for instance, a "green receptor" version, a "blue receptor" version and a "UV receptor" version. The brain can integrate the three pixels to produce "color."

Can Insects "See" Color?

Many insects can discriminate colors including honeybees. Color vision can be demonstrated experimentally. Bees given sugar water in front of only one of two different color panels will learn to orient to a single color that is associated with the food. For example, a sugar solution is placed in front of a blue panel and an empty dish is placed in front of a yellow panel. After training, honeybees will orient to the blue panel first and not the yellow one, even after food is placed in front of both. The trained bees will orient to the blue panel if the locations change.

The minimum requirement for color vision is two photoreceptor types that differ in wavelength sensitivity. Color vision in humans results from three visual receptors (cones) that differ in sensitivity. Each type of photoreceptor transmits a light/dark pixel to the brain according to the receptor sensitivity. The brain integrates the three pixels that are experienced as "color." For example an object that we would see as blue would create a light pattern from the "blue" receptors, but dark patterns from both the green and red receptors. An object that we would see as "green" would create a lighter pattern from the green receptors and darker patterns from red and blue receptors. The brain integrates the light and dark information from each receptor type to create the sensation of color. Color is a sensation of the brain, not intrinsic property of object. We doubt that insects "experience" color the same way that humans do. In fact, not all people experience color the same way.

Insects commonly differ from humans in having vision that is responsive to light in the UV range, but not responsive to red light. Many insects cannot distinguish red from black. However, objects that appear to humans as "blue" may appear to insects to have a pattern in the UV.

Polarized Light

Some insects are capable of detecting polarized light. Light waves from the sun are polarized when they hit the atmosphere. Detection of polarized light enables insects to determine the direction of the sun, even on cloudy days. The sun is important for orientation, especially among insects that nest. Humans cannot readily discriminate polarized light without aids such as polarizing filters. Polarized sunglasses work because the "glare" (scattered light) is polarized. Eliminating the light polarized in the direction of the glare with a filter allows us to see only the non-scattered light (polarized in the perpendicular directions. Polarization while invisible to people is visible to many insects including honey bees.

Patterns, Not Objects

It is unlikely that the insect visual systems form objects in the same way that the human visual system can form "objects." "Visual objects" are a created by our brain. Object creation requires a very large capacity for processing visual information. Insect lack the requisite brain cells to visualize objects. Instead, insects rely on a more primitive information system of optic flow. People use optic flow information to process movement. However, the process is so basic and innate, most people do not think about it.

Optic Flow

Optic flow is the movement of patterns across the visual receptors. Insects use optic flow for determining distances to objects and adjusting flight speed. A more rapid rate of optic flow indicates that an object is closer. If an insect doubles its flight speed, the optic flow doubles. Optic flow increases as distance to an object decreases. Patterns that are 90 degrees to the direction of movement have the fastest optic flow. Patterns that are directly ahead or directly behind (zero or 180 degrees) have zero optic flow.

As an insect moves forward, patterns that the insect will pass "flow" to edges of the visual field. Patterns that are on a collision course do not move, but expand across the visual field. The central point of a pattern on a collision course is called the focus of expansion. This expansion can be experienced by holding a pattern directly in front of you and moving it toward your eyes.

In most insects, the eyes are stationary and the head, or whole body must turn. Optic flow is in the opposite direction of a turn. As an insect rotates clockwise, optic flow rotates counterclockwise. If an insect is hovering, all optic flow is zero (no pattern movement across the visual field). If the environment is moving (tree branches swaying in the wind) achieving zero optic flow will cause the insect to adjust to the movements of the branch and "hover" relative to the branch instead of the ground.

Collisions

Optic flow is useful for avoiding collisions. A large optic flow indicates an object is close. Insects will reduce flight speed or move away from the object to slow optic flow. For an insect landing on an object such as a flower, the object will be the focus of expansion. If the insect keeps the rate of the expansion constant, the insect will slow down as it approaches and lands on the object.

The advantage of using optic flow pattern information over object information is the more rapid processing of optic flow information. Fast flying insects need fast, real-time information to avoid collisions. The flicker rate, or the rate that the visual system can process signals is more rapid in insects compared to humans. This avoids motion blur, important for fast flying insects. Other adaptations for flight include having compound eyes directed at all angles. Flying insects such as dragonflies have 360-degree vision.

Do insects see in three dimensions? Not necessarily. Patterns alone are sufficient for judging distances and avoiding collisions.

Uses for Insect Vision Studies?

Why is insect vision of such interest? Because insects use fewer brain cells to process information, simulating insect vision is less complicated and would require less computer processing power than trying to simulate object discrimination ability of humans. Along with the faster information processing of patterns, optic flow and insect vision simulation may be useful for remote guidance systems of robots.

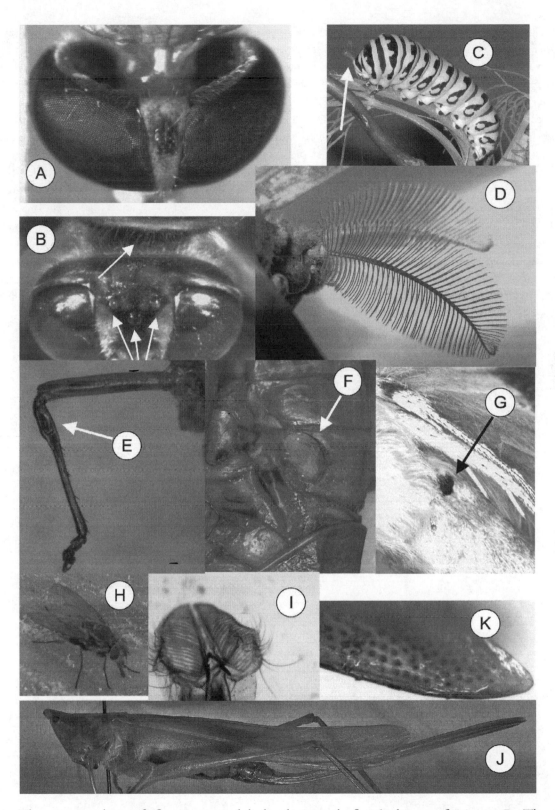

A. The compound eyes of a fly wrap around the head, giving the fly 360 degrees of vision.   B. Three ocelli are located between the compound eyes on the top of a wasp head. Ocelli can detect light intensity, but do not form images. Hairs between the head and the thorax provide information to the wasp about its flight attitude relative to gravity. When the wasp is facing downward, gravity increases the gap between the head and the thorax. When the wasp is facing upward, gravity decreases the gap between the head and the thorax. The sensory hairs respond to the gap.   C. A caterpillar of the black swallowtail butterfly displays its osmeterium (arrow) when disturbed. The osmeterium is a defensive gland that produces malodorous butyric acid to deter predators.   D. Antennae of male saturniid moths are branched to provide an extended platform for the large numbers of pheromone receptors. Antennae sweep chemicals from the air. Odor producing chemicals dissolve in the liquid in the interior of the antenna and interact with odor receptors.   E. Sound detection organ on the leg of a katydid. Many insects detect sound with a tympanum, a vibrating membrane (like the head of a drum). Katydid sound detectors are on the front legs.   F. A tympanum (sound detector) on the first abdominal segment of a grasshopper (wings removed).   G. A tympanum on the abdomen of a moth. Moths use their tympanum to detect bat sonar. Bats are important predators of night-flying moths.   H. A fly feeding on tree sap. Flies have taste receptors on their feet and on their mouthparts. Receptors on the feet allow flies to detect small patches of sugar and other food as they run across surfaces.   I. A close up of the housefly "sponging type mouthparts. Sensory hairs on the mouthparts may be sensitive to touch, or taste- bitter, sweet, salt and sour.   J. Sword-like ovipositor of the Cone-headed grasshopper is used for laying eggs in plant stems.   K. The tips of the Cone-headed grasshopper ovipositor contain taste receptors that provide information of the identity and quality of the plant pierced by the ovipositor.

Chapter 7 Study Questions

1. Where are insect taste receptors located?

2. What chemicals do insects taste?

3. Are insect sweet receptors the same as human sweet receptors?

4. How does the internal state of a blowfly (hungry versus satiated) affect its decision to feed on a sugar solution?

5. What effect does adding bitter substances to the sugar solution have on blowfly feeding?

6. Describe the process that must occur for an insect to detect an odor?

7. How do insects use odors for communication?

8. What is sound?

9. How do crickets and katydids produce chirps?

10. How do cicadas produce sound?

11. How do moths detect sound?

12. Why is sound detection important to moths?

13. What types of simple eyes to insects have?

14. Do insects see color?

15. Do insects see the same colors that people see?

16. How do insects use optic flow?

17. Do insect brains create three-dimensional objects?

18. How does a faster flicker frequency help flying insects?

Chapter 8

Insect Orientation Behaviors

Orientation

Orientation behaviors guide an animal at one location to another location. The orientation process requires feedback from external cues that inform the movement. Arriving at a location or "finding" the location requires that the movement stop.

Orientation By Landmarks

Orientation by landmarks is a complex method of orientation, but it is the one most commonly used by people who know where they are going. Orientation by landmarks requires remembering a series of cues, and moving in the proper direction with respect to those cues.

For example, if you were finishing lunch at Harry's Chocolate Shop and going to attend a class in Matthews Hall, you would orient by landmarks. The first landmark would be the front door of Harry's. As you leave Harry's you notice Main Street, a second and long landmark. You turn in the direction of Rawls Hall (another landmark) and pass several landmarks along the route. These landmarks may include, Krannert, The Union, Stewart Center, Stone Hall, and finally Matthews Hall at the corner of University and State Street. The front doors are a landmark as are the stairs. When you reach the top of the stairs, you can see the door to the auditorium, another landmark. The seats are other landmarks. You chose a suitable seat. When you arrive at your seat, you have "found" your way to class and you stop moving and sit down.

Orientation by landmarks requires that you memorize visual images that you "recognize" as landmarks and have a mental map of the spatial relationship of those images. You "orient" using the visual feedback from the landmarks.

Insects and Landmarks

Most insects do NOT use landmarks because insects rarely "know" their final destination until they arrive. In fact, most insects have no experience of their destination until they arrive. Among insects that "know where they are going" in advance are insects that build nests. Nest-building insects often use landmarks to find the nest. Orientation by landmarks is especially common among the Hymenoptera (wasps). Both social and solitary Hymenoptera may use landmarks to locate nesting sites.

Sand Wasps and Landmarks

Sand wasps are solitary wasps that build nests in the sand. A female sand wasp will dig a nest, and then fly off to find a prey item. On the departing flight, the wasp performs a circling flight of the area for the purpose of memorizing landmarks. Other landmarks are noted along the journey.

The Dutch scientist, Niko Tinbergen, observed and experimented with burrowing sand wasps. He watched a female wasp digging a nest and waited until she had disappeared into the tunnel. While the female was in the tunnel, he surrounded the opening with a ring of pine cones to serve as landmarks. When the wasp flew off to find prey it performed its circling flight to memorize the landmarks. After capturing prey, the wasp returned to the ring of pine cones. Because the pine cones were not present when the female first chose the nest site, it was clear that the landmarks were memorized only upon leaving the nest.

Tinbergen then watched another wasp build a nest. He surrounded the entrance with pine cones while the wasp was in the nest. After the wasp had left the nest and flown out of sight to hunt prey, Tinbergen moved the ring of pine cones to a nearby location. The wasp returned to the ring of pine cones (landmarks) instead of to the burrow entrance. The female wasp was unable to locate the burrow that she had just dug because the pine cone landmarks had been moved. This demonstrated that the female wasps were memorizing landmarks to locate their burrow during the flight away from the freshly dug burrow.

Similarly, ants, social bees, and wasps memorize landmarks upon leaving the nest so they will be able to return.

Orientation Without Landmarks

Most insects cannot orient using landmarks because they are not familiar with the territory and need to locate resources that are unknown to them. In the absence of landmarks, insects often use other orientation mechanisms such as orthokinesis and klinokinesis. Humans use these orientation mechanisms, which are innate.

Orthokinesis is a change in speed in response to stimulus.
Klinokinesis is a change in rate of turning in response to stimulus.

Imagine walking the streets of a strange city, hungry and not knowing where to get something to eat. You walk very rapidly past the bad smelling waste treatment facility (not likely to find something to eat there!). As you enter the business district, you smell the odor of baked goods. What do you do? You slow down. This is "orthokinesis," a change in speed in response to stimulus. If the odor is bad, you walk faster. If the odor is good, you walk slower.

Now that you smell the odor of baked goods, you not only slow down. You also more intensively "search" the area to locate the source of the odor. This intensive search involves departing from the straight line you were previously walking (that led from one area of the city to another) and increasing the frequency of turning as you go from one shop to the next to locate the shop with the baked goods. This is "klinokinesis," change in rate of turning in response to stimulus.

A visitor to the new city could locate a bakery without any prior knowledge that the city even had a bakery. Landmarks could not be used because the city was unfamiliar. The bakery could be located by a combination of orthokinesis and klinokinesis in response to environmental cues.

Insect Orientation

Many insects are like our visitor. They lack foreknowledge of the location of resources that they need. However, by using simple feedback from environmental cues, they are able to find resources.

Orthokinesis in cockroaches. Cockroaches hide in cracks and crevices and avoid lights. If you enter a cockroach-infested apartment and turn on the lights, the cockroaches will respond to the light by rapidly increasing the rate of speed. Their movements are not directed. They turn erratically and randomly. By increasing their speed of travel, cockroaches will more rapidly leave the open, unsheltered areas. Once they have moved (at random) into a dark crevice they decrease their rate of speed. They have "found" a crevice.

Insects locating food or oviposition sites may also use a combination of orthokinesis and klinokinesis. An important strategy for insects is to move when resources are lacking (bad neighborhoods) and to stay when resources are abundant (good neighborhoods).

Orientation By Odor

Odors are not uniform or consistent. In an enclosed environment, the odor may permeate the entire area making it difficult to locate the source. In open spaces, movement of odors depends on the rate of diffusion. Molecules with small molecular size diffuse rapidly. Molecules with larger molecular size will diffuse more slowly and travel in a plume, an elongated cone that slowly widens and dissipates as it moves away from the source. Odors generally travel downwind, but do not travel in a straight line because the wind is not constant in direction and often shifts. How do insects like male moths use very erratic odor cues to locate females that may be a mile away?

Optomotor Anemotaxis

Optomotor anemotaxis is the mechanism that a moth uses to follow an odor plume. The wind, not the odor provides the direction. A male moth that detects a female pheromone flies generally upwind but at an angle to the true upwind. When the moth leaves the odor plume it makes a turn back across the wind. If it flies back into the odor plume, the moth will maintain course until it leaves the plume on the other side. Then it will make another turn. Instead of flying straight up the odor plume (impossible because of shifts in the wind) the male flies at an angle upwind back and forth across the plume, making a turn each time it leaves the plume that will bring it back into contact with the plume upwind from where it left.

If the moth loses contact with the odor for an extended period, it will fly in ever wider "casting flights" and move slightly downwind to relocate the odor. Insects judge their airspeed and forward progress relative to ground patterns moving past the visual field (to be discussed later). Optomotor anemotaxis requires that the male moth be able to detect the wind direction, fly upwind and use odor detection to adjust its upwind flight.

Know Where To Go?

Typically, insects will leave an area if there are not adequate resources. If they do not or cannot leave, they die. If an area contains adequate resources, insects will stay. Typically, we find insects in a habitat that contains adequate resources. However, finding the insects in their habitat says nothing about how the insects arrived in that habitat or the finding process. Insects may not know where they are going, but they know where they are staying.

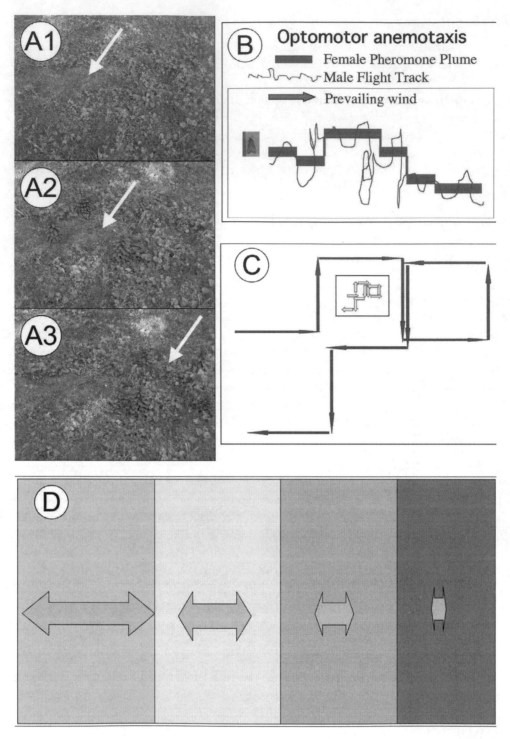

A. Recreation of the Tinbergen, sand wasp experiment. 1. The wasp builds a nest (arrow), flies off to find a prey and returns to the nest. 2. While the wasp is in the nest (arrow) Tinbergen surrounded the nest with pine cones. The wasp returned to the nest with the prey. 3. While the wasp is in the nest (arrow) Tinbergen surrounded the nest with pine cones. After the wasp left the nest and was out of sight, Tinberg moved the pine cones. The wasp returned with the prey to the new location of the pine cones and was unable to locate the nest. Conclusion: After the wasp completes its nest, it makes a circling flight. It is during the circling flight that the wasp memorizes

(*continued on page 93*)

Consider the squash bug that spends the winter as an adult at the edge of a field. In early summer, the adults become active and must locate a squash plant to reproduce. Squash bugs will feed on most plant species for at least short times and obtain water and some nutrients. This will nourish the squash bug on its journey, but will not allow it to reproduce. If the plant is not a squash plant, the bug will feed a little, then move on. The squash bug will repeat this process until it reaches a squash plant. Then it will stay, feed a lot, mate and lay eggs. The squash bug does not "know" where it is going, but when it is on a squash plant, it knows that it is staying.

Random Search

Some insects such as aphids produce enormous numbers of progeny. At the end of summer, the plants the aphids are feeding upon decline and die. The aphids cannot survive if they remain, so they leave in a random search for overwintering sites. Most of the aphids die during the process of finding an over-wintering site. However, the very large numbers ensure that some individuals will find the resource even while most are dying. The random search is not very efficient. However, this lack of efficiency can be overcome with large numbers.

Applications of Insect Orientation Behaviors

Studies of orientation in insects can be applied to efforts to develop robots with artificial intelligence. By studying how insects are able to locate resources and understanding the underlying mechanisms, we can try to impart those mechanisms to our machines. Many of the mechanisms that humans use to orient are innate and can be performed without much introspection. Studies of insect behavior and orientation mechanisms shed more light on mechanisms that we use but may easily overlook.

(plate caption *continued*)

the landmarks needed to return to the nest.   B. Male moths use optomotor anemotaxis to orient upwind to the female. The female pheromone (bar) hangs in a plume that is blown down wind. Sensing the pheromone, the male moth makes a flight track (line) upwind. If the moth is in contact with the pheromone plume, it will fly generally upwind. When the moth loses the pheromone plume, it will make casting flights perpendicular to the wind direction until the plume is relocated. The plume is not a straight line because of changes in wind direction and wind currents flowing around objects.   C. Klinokinesis is a change in the rate of turning in response to a stimulus. The track in the small inner box makes one turn for every 2 distance units. This makes the search area smaller and more intense. The track outside the small box makes one turn for every 14 distance units. This increases the search area, but decreases the search intensity. Decreasing the rate of turning to zero will cause the insect to leave the area.   D. Orthokinesis is a change in the rate of movement in response to a stimulus. In the figure, the rate of movement in each box decreases from left to right. The response to an attractant is to decrease the rate of movement. The response to a repellent is an increase in the rate of movement.

Chapter 8 Study Questions

1. How do insects with nests orient to the nest?

2. What is orthokinesis?

3. What is klinokinesis?

4. How do insects use orthokinesis and klinokinesis to locate unknown resources?

5. How do cockroaches use orthokinesis to return to cracks and crevices?

6. Is it possible to orient to an odor solely by following a concentration gradient?

7. How do most flying insects arrive at odor sources?

8. What process does a squash bug use to arrive at a host plant?

Chapter 9

Notable Groups of Insects

Beetles

What Does the Name "Coleoptera" Mean?

All beetles belong to the insect order Coleoptera. The Greek scientist, Aristotle, gave them the name "Coleoptera," which means "sheath (cole) wing (optera)." The forewings of adult beetles (called elytra) meet (without overlapping) in a straight line down the middle of the back. The elytra are made of a hard protein that protects the hind wings (like a sheath) when the beetle is not flying. The elytra allow adult beetles to move in close contact with plants and other objects without damaging their delicate, membranous hind wings.

How Do Beetles Fly?

The forewings are not used to power beetles in flight. Instead, the forewings are held up and out of the way (like the open hood of an auto) during flight. Only the membranous hind wings beat up and down. Most beetles are rather clumsy fliers.

What Life Stages Do Beetles Have?

Beetles have complete metamorphosis with an egg, several larval stages, a pupa, and an adult stage. Complete metamorphosis allows the adults and larvae to evolve adaptive characters independently. The larvae are adapted to growth and feeding. The adults are adapted to movement and reproduction. The transformation from larva to adult occurs within the pupa. The pupa stage of beetles is immobile and vulnerable. Beetles often pupate in areas that give some protection from predators such as in tunnels in the soil or wood.

How Do Beetles Eat?

The larvae and adults of Coleoptera have chewing mouthparts. This contrasts with other insect groups with complete metamorphosis (such as Lepidoptera and Diptera) that commonly have different types of mouthparts as larvae and adults.

What Do Beetle Larvae Look Like?

Beetle larvae have a wide diversity of shapes that vary among the families of beetles. Some beetle larvae have short abdomens and can walk on their legs and hold their abdomen off the ground such as predatory ground beetles. Some plant-feeding beetle larvae with extended abdomens rest the abdomen on a surface. Some beetle larvae, such as the C-shaped grubs, crawl through the soil. A number of beetles live in trees and those larvae often have an elongated abdomen. The wide diversity of larval forms mirrors the wide diversity of habitats and feeding strategies of the beetle larvae.

When Did the First Beetles Appear?

The fossil record of the beetles dates to the Permian period (286–250 mya). During the extinction event that marks the end of the Permian around 250 mya, many of the insect species and groups went extinct in a relatively short period of time. The beetles survived the extinction event and were well adapted to the post-extinction environment. The beetles rapidly diversified to occupy the many newly empty habitats.

How Many Beetle Species?

Today, beetles are the largest group of insects. Over 300,000 species of beetles have been described. The largest (mass) insect is the Titan beetle that can weigh over 100 grams and reach 170 millimeters in length. The smallest insect is also a beetle that is about one quarter of a millimeter long and weighs less than half a milligram. The range from smallest to largest beetle is over five orders of magnitude (0.4 to 10,000 mg). Not only is there a huge range in size of beetles from smallest to largest, but also beetles are adapted to almost every habitat on the planet excepting the oceans and the frozen areas.

Where Do Beetles Live?

There are beetles that live beneath the soil, in caves, on the ground, in stems of plants, and in living tree trunks. Beetles live in rotting logs, on foliage of trees, and herbaceous plants, within seeds, and on flowers. Many beetles feed on pollen as a source of protein and are important pollinators of plants.

Some beetles are scavengers that feed on the carcasses of dead animals. Other scavengers specialize on the fur and skin of animals or woolen items. Dung beetles feed on manure produced by mammals. Some beetles feed on dead plant material. Many beetles feed on fungi and can be found between the veins underneath the caps of mushrooms.

Not all beetles live on land. Some beetles are aquatic, adapted for life in fresh water. There are beetles that swim on top of the water, swim in the water, or live on the soil at the bottom of streams.

Why So Many Beetle Species?

The large number of species is directly related to the wide variety of habitats that can support a beetle species. Compared to the habitats of large vertebrates, insects can be described as having "microhabitats" or places of specialization within a larger habitat. Humans think of habitats as large units such as a forest or a corn field. To small insects, however, our habitats may contain numerous "microhabitats."

The wide range of beetle size enables beetles to adapt to new habitats. For example, there are beetles that complete their entire development within a bean seed. There are similar beetles that can complete their development within a much smaller rice grain. We find one species of beetle adapted to rice grains and another to corn kernels. With all the different types of seeds available, there are thousands of habitats available for seed beetles.

If we multiply the number of species of plants by the number of microhabitats (roots, stems, seeds, etc) the number of microhabitats that can support a beetle species is enormous. Adding those microhabitats to the thousands more available to beetles that are predatory, scavengers, or aquatic produce more than the required number of microhabitats to support over 300,000 species of beetle.

Do Beetles Spread Diseases?

Unlike the flies that feed upon and colonize live mammals, beetles do not attack people or other mammals. For that reason beetles are not known to transmit human diseases through their activities. However, beetles do feed upon plants and are important carriers of plant diseases.

Dutch elm disease is a fungus that is spread by wood boring beetles. Dutch elm disease killed millions of elm trees across the United States in the 1950s and 1960s. Very few native American elms survived this devastating disease. Elms were very popular shade trees and commonly planted along the streets and roadsides. Old pictures of the John Purdue Mall feature large elm trees. Today, those majestic elms are gone, victims of the Dutch elm disease. The elms are distant memories that have been replaced by other species of trees, less majestic but more disease resistant.

Dutch elm disease is not the only disease carried by beetles. Ambrosia beetles that bore into tree trunks carry fungus that grows in the galleries created by the beetles. Ambrosia beetles feed on the fungus, not the tree itself. Some pine beetles carry fungus that blocks the ability of the tree to pitch the beetles out.

Spotted cucumber beetles that feed on squash and cucumber can carry a bacteria that enters the plant through a feeding site and causes the vines to wilt, killing the plant. These beetles are a major pest of squash and melons grown in much of the United States.

Common Beetles

Lady Beetles

Lady beetles are brightly colored beetles (typically red or yellow) with dark spots. Most people are familiar with lady beetles because they are active during the day and have noticeably bright colors. Although they are called "lady beetles" they are both male and female.

Lady beetles are considered beneficial because they eat aphids and other small insects that damage plants. Lady beetles are predators as larvae and adults. Lady beetle larvae have large forward-facing mandibles that they use to impale and chew their prey. Lady beetles are sold to organic gardeners as biological control agents.

Our native species of lady beetles prefer to overwinter outdoors. However, a recent immigrant, the Asian lady beetle aggregates indoors. When the temperature starts to cool in autumn, the adults seek sheltered overwintering sites. They enter cracks and crevices and often work their way into our homes. They are harmless, but most people prefer not to have them in their home. Entomology departments receive many complaints every year about the beetles.

Lady beetle control. The beetles are easily removed with a vacuum. I recommend vacuuming the beetles, and removing the vacuum bag to release the beetles outside. If the vacuum bag with the collected beetles is left indoors, the beetles will crawl out of the bag, down the hose, and back into the house.

Firefly

Many people are familiar with the firefly, the state insect of Indiana. On warm summer nights, fireflies fill the air with their flashing lights. Fireflies are associated with relaxing summer evenings and romantic moments on the porch swing. Slow and ponderous fliers, they are easy to capture. Fireflies provide entertainment for children who catch them in jars and release them. In the 1950s and 1960s, NASA sponsored research to discover how fireflies produce light and paid people to collect and send them fireflies. Many children participated in this program.

A light organ in the abdomen produces the firefly light flash. The light organ contains a chemical, luciferin. When luciferin is mixed with oxygen and ATP (an energy source) in the presence of the enzyme luciferase, a chemical reaction occurs that releases photons (that we see as light). The enzyme and chemicals can be produced artificially. Most people are familiar with glow sticks that contain synthetic luciferin and glow in the dark.

Most firefly larvae and adults are predators. The larvae eat snails, slugs, and other small prey items. Firefly larvae as well as adults may glow. Firefly larvae are called "glow worms." Many firefly larvae are distasteful or toxic and the glow of the larvae may be a warning signal to potential predators.

Firefly adults use light flashes to communicate with each other. Each species of firefly has its own code. The males flash a code as they fly through the air. Females typically wait on a bush or the ground. Females flash a return code to males of the same species. A male and female will signal back and forth to each other until the male reaches the female. The different codes ensure that a male finds a female of the same species for mating.

All is not love in the tiny flickers of light sent by fireflies. Female fireflies of the genus *Photuris* prey upon male fireflies of other species through a bit of trickery. Thus they are called "femme fatales."

A femme fatale *Photuris* firefly can mimic the flash code of other species of fireflies. If a femme fatale *Photuris* female sees a flash from a *Photinus* species male, she will flash a code that mimics the female *Photinus* instead of her own *Photuris* flash code. Responding "to his newly found true love calling to him," the *Photinus* male flies and lands next to the *Photuris* female. Instead of finding a "true love" *Photinus* female mate, the unlucky male *Photinus* finds a *Photuris* "femme fatale" predator who promptly eats him. Why do *Photuris* females need to eat *Photinus* males? *Photinus* males contain a defensive chemical that *Photuris* females are unable to make. *Photuris* females sequester the defensive chemical from their *Photinus* male prey and use it to protect their eggs.

Fireflies with rhythm. In Southeast Asia, there are species of fireflies that congregate on bushes along the riverbanks. An internal timing system causes all the males to flash in synchrony. These synchronous fireflies perform fantastic light shows making the riverbanks flash off and on like Christmas trees.

Seed Weevils

The weevils are one of the largest groups of beetles (over 60,000 species). One group of weevils, the seed weevils are tiny beetles that completely develop inside a single seed. Seed weevils are important pests of our stored grains such as corn and rice. Seed weevil females lay one egg on each seed. The egg hatches and the larva tunnels into the seed. Females mark the outside of the seed with a chemical scent as a reminder to not lay an egg on an occupied seed. Marking the eggs prevents competition and ensures that a larva has enough food to complete development. The seed provides both food and protection for the larva. The larva pupates within the seed and chews its way out as an adult.

Boll Weevil

Boll weevil is an important pest of cotton. Boll weevil adults will chew a hole into the unopened flowers of cotton (the bolls), lay an egg in the hole, and seal it with a secretion. The larva hatches and consumes much of the unopened flower. After the damaged flower opens, it is shed from the plant. Since the cotton flowers are used for making cloth, the boll weevil can greatly reduce cotton yield.

Boll weevil migrated into the southeastern United States from Mexico in 1915. Boll weevil damage made growing cotton unprofitable in some places. There are numerous blues songs written about the boll weevil.

In Enterprise, Alabama, farmers responded by diversifying their crops and planting alternatives such as peanuts. The diversification was successful and farmers were able to make money again. The boll weevil destroyed their cotton, but diversification led to better profits. The citizens erected a statue in tribute to the boll weevil in 1919. Unfortunately the statue has been a target of vandals who on several occasions have stolen the boll weevil and damaged the original statue. The original statue is now safeguarded in a secure location and has been replaced by a replica.

Recently, national projects have successfully eradicated boll weevil from many of the cotton growing states. Eradication reduces the costs of growing cotton (applying pesticides is expensive) and simplifies management of other cotton pests. Monitoring traps baited with boll weevil pheromone are used to detect re-infestation. If boll weevil returns to an area, intensive efforts will be made within the small area to eradicate the newly appearing populations and prevent their spread.

Stag Beetle

The stag beetle family contains some large beetles known for males with large mandibles that resemble the antlers of stags (male deer). The larvae of stag beetles live in rotting logs and feed on wood. The larvae develop very slowly and are time consuming to rear.

Most stag beetles are territorial. Male stag beetles use oversized mandibles use to guard mates and spar with other males. Males can lock mandibles and wrestle each other for territory and mates. Stag beetles are popular among collectors. Some stag beetles reportedly fetch thousands of dollars. In some countries collectors stage fights among male stag beetles and gamble on the contest.

Sexton Beetle

The sexton beetle colonizes dead animals such as mice and other small rodents. Males and females compete for small carcasses. A successful male and female pair will move soil from underneath the carcass until the carcass is buried. The pair will mate on the carcass and prepare it for the offspring. Females treat the carcass with secretions that prevent microbes from growing. Burying the carcass sequesters the resource and allows the parents to keep competitors away from their offspring. The parents will guard the carcass from other beetles that would eat their offspring and take over the carcass. In some species, the female will chew the food and feed it to small larvae. The small larvae have mandibles too small to efficiently chew the carcass. Parental care increases the rates of larval development and survival.

Tiger Beetles

The tiger beetles are a family of beetles that are predatory both as a larva and adult. Adult tiger beetles have long legs to chase down prey by running fast (like tigers). Tiger beetle mandibles are like sharp swords that impale their prey.

Many tiger beetle larvae dig burrows. The larvae wait for prey to appear near the entrance. The larvae will snatch the prey with their mouthparts. Hooks on their abdomen anchor the larvae inside the tunnel. Some tiger beetle larvae specialize on small insects such as ants. Other tiger beetle larvae can capture prey much larger than themselves. They drag their prey items into their burrow where they can feed, protected from larger predators.

Japanese Beetle

The Japanese beetle is an invasive species that came to United States on nursery stock from Japan in the early 1900s. The Japanese beetle originally arrived in New Jersey and has since spread across the eastern United States. There are ongoing efforts to keep it out of western states.

Japanese beetle adults feed on flowers and are especially destructive of roses. Adults will also feed on grape leaves and leaves of ornamental trees. Japanese beetles are attracted to flower odors and release pheromones to attract other beetles. Mating takes place on flowers, often in large groups. The pheromones and floral scent are produced synthetically for use in commercial Japanese beetle traps. The traps capture and kill numerous beetles but are not effective at control or preventing damage.

Japanese beetles have **C-shaped larvae** called **grubs**. The grubs live in soil and feed on the roots of grass. They are important pests of lawns and golf courses. The larvae over-winter by burrowing deep into the soil below where it freezes. In spring they resume feeding and emerge as adults in early summer.

Grubs can also be a major problem in athletic facilities and stadiums with natural grass. Grubs can destroy the grass roots so the grass pulls up in clumps and creates poor footing. Japanese beetle larvae are primarily controlled using insecticides or in some cases, fungal diseases.

Dung Beetles

Animal dung (or manure) is a rich source of nutrients. Dung contains partially digested plant material and other nutrients. There is intense competition for dung among insects.

Dung beetles will specialize on manure from specific animals. Some dung beetles specialize on the dung of small animals. These animals may produce only enough dung for a single larva. Dung beetles may lay an egg on the dung and bury it on the spot.

Dung beetles that specialize on the dung of larger animals often encounter a dung pile that is too large for a single beetle or a mated pair to bury. These dung beetles arrive at a large manure pie and collect enough dung to feed a larva from egg to adult. The dung beetles roll the manure into a ball and roll it to another site for burial. The dung beetle buries the manure ball, lays an egg on it and seals it underground with soil. This gives the dung beetle larva plenty of food for development without competition from other dung beetles or other insects such as flies.

Dung beetles keep us from being knee deep in dung. When cattle were first imported to Australia in the 1700s the cow manure was not used by the native dung beetles. The native species were adapted to kangaroos and other Australian animals and not cattle. The cow dung accumulated, fouling millions of hectares of pasture. The cow manure was a huge breeding ground for flies, enough to produce hundreds of billions of flies daily. To solve the problem, the Australians imported dung beetles from Europe and Africa. The imported dung beetle species that adapted to cattle dung processed the manure and decreased the fly population.

Religious symbol. The dung beetle appears in several cultures as a religious symbol. The dung beetle habit of rolling balls and its appearance as an adult from its underground burrow is the basis of the ancient Egyptian story of Khepri, the scarab god of the sun. In legend, the scarab god, Khepri, rolled the sun across the sky each day and buried it in the soil each evening. The scarab beetle is an iconic symbol that appears in Egyptian hieroglyphs. Roman soldiers adopted the scarab symbol, commonly used as amulets.

Bombardier Beetle
The bombardier beetle is noted for its special chemical defense. Many insects will release chemicals for defense against ants and other predators. However, the bombardier beetle has a special reaction chamber at the tip of its abdomen for a heat-producing chemical reaction. Within the chamber, chemicals and enzymes mix to create a boiling hot liquid that is sprayed on the attacker. While the spray is boiling hot, the beetle produces only small amounts at a time for immediate release. This prevents the beetle from scalding itself and damaging its cells. The tip of the abdomen is flexible and forms a "spray nozzle" around the opening to the chamber. The beetle can aim the spray for maximum effectiveness. The hot liquid is very deterrent to smaller predators such as ants.

Summary

The beetles are a very large and diverse group of insects. Their adult body plan is adaptable for a large range of sizes. Beetles have adapted to a large variety of different foods. They have adapted to the habitats ranging from aquatic to the driest deserts. Because of their abundance, beetles are familiar to most people. Beetles are often a favorite of children because they are non-threatening. Beetles are common characters in children's books and songs. Beetles have very important roles in our ecosystem. The above account is only of a small taste of a few of the more familiar or unique species. Our world is filled with vast numbers of beetle species with a great variety of interesting life histories.

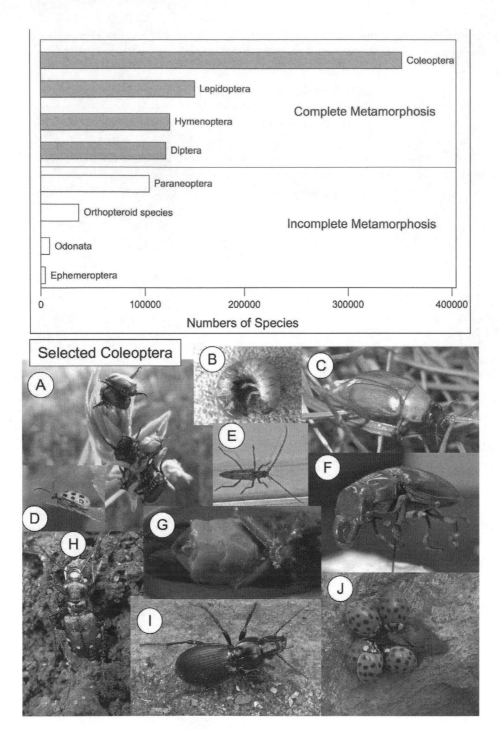

Figure. Coleoptera are the most numerous type of insect, comprising about one third of the described species. The most successful groups (ones with the largest numbers of species) all have complete metamorphosis. A larval feeding stage with characters that can evolve separately from the adult dispersal and mating stage is important to the success of these groups.

A. Japanese Beetles are an invasive species that damage ornamental plants. Beetles aggregate on flowers, attracted to plant fragrance and pheromones of other beetles, and commonly mate in groups.   B. A grub is one type of beetle larva. Grubs live in the soil and feed on the roots of plants. Japanese beetle grubs feed on the roots of grass and damage lawns and golf courses.   C. A chafer is another beetle that feeds on plants. Note the membranous hind

(*continued on page 107*)

Lepidoptera: Moths and Butterflies

History of Lepidoptera

There are over 150,000 species of Lepidoptera. The Lepidoptera are the most recent of the large orders of insects to evolve. Lepidoptera evolved in the Cretaceous Period over 100 million years ago. Much of the diversity of this group was coincident with the evolution of flowering plants. Lepidoptera survived the extinction event 65 million years ago (mya) that eliminated the dinosaurs and have continued to diversify since then.

What Life Stages Do Lepidoptera Have?

Lepidoptera have complete metamorphosis—egg, larva, pupa, and adult. The larvae of Lepidoptera are called "caterpillars." The pupa of a moth is called a cocoon. The pupa of a butterfly is called a chrysalis.

What Does the Name "Lepidoptera" Mean?

The name "Lepidoptera" is from the Latin "Lepido" meaning "scale" and "ptera" meaning "wing." The wings of butterflies and moths are coated with extensions of the cuticle called scales. The scales are loosely attached to the cuticle of the wings and are easily rubbed off. Improper handling can destroy butterfly and moth specimens by inadvertently removing scales.

The wings of Lepidoptera are formed by an upper and lower row of epidermal cells that are closely apposed. The epidermal cells secrete the top and bottom cuticular surface of the wings and the scales. In specific parts of the wing, the cells are thickened and separated by a space that forms a tube. These spaces are the "wing veins" of Lepidoptera. The wing veins provide rigidity to the wing and allow fluid into the wings. The fluid makes the wings of live Lepidoptera flexible. Wings of pinned specimens of butterflies and moths dry and become brittle and inflexible.

What are the Differences Between Butterflies and Moths?

The majority (95 percent) of Lepidoptera are moths. Butterflies are a smaller subgroup with shared characteristics. Butterfly and moth adults both have wings with scales and mouthparts that are formed into a long tube for sipping nectar (a liquid) from flowers. Typically, butterflies have knobs on the ends of their antennae. Moths have a variety of antennae shapes, but they are never knobbed at the end. Butterflies are typically active during the day, while most moths are nocturnal (there are exceptions). The thorax and abdomen of moths are typically more robust than these body regions of butterflies.

(plate caption *continued*)

---

wing protruding beyond the hard protective front wings (elytra). Beetles have a special mechanism for folding the hind wings. Adult beetles can be recognized by the elytra that meet in a straight line down the top of the abdomen without overlap.   D. A spotted-cucumber beetle rests on a leaf. These beetles will feed on cucumber and squash and can transmit a bacteria that causes plants to wilt.   E. Long-horned (Cerambicid) beetles feed on wood as larvae. The long antennae are used by male beetles to help locate mates.   F. Stag beetles also feed on wood as larvae. Note the enlarged mandibles. Male stag beetles use the large mandibles to fight other male beetles, establish territory and guard females from mating with other males.   G. The abdomen of the firefly contains a light organ that glows due to a chemical reaction. Fireflies use their light organs to locate and communicate with potential mates.   H. A six-spotted tiger beetle is a predator that can run down slower moving prey.   I. Ground beetles are common predators that typically hunt at night.   J. Lady beetles are feeding on sap oozing from a tree. Lady beetles are predators as larvae and adults feeding on aphids and other soft bodied insects. They supplement their diet of prey with natural sources of sugar.

How are Lepidoptera Identified?

The character commonly used to group butterflies and moths into families are the wings. Wings have "veins" or tubes that allow hemolymph to pass through them. The veins form a pattern that is consistent within related groups of butterflies and moths. Some families of butterflies and moths have coloration or wing shapes that are characteristic of the group. For example, the swallowtail butterflies are large and have a characteristic "tail" on the tip of the hind wings. The cabbage butterflies all have yellow or white coloration that has a powdery appearance.

How are Lepidoptera Specimens Collected?

Butterflies and moths are fragile and commonly damaged before they can be collected. Collectors prefer perfect specimens and will go to lengths to produce them. Collectors frequently collect caterpillars or eggs and rear caterpillars to adults. The popular Morpho butterfly is nearly impossible to catch as it flies among the treetops. Most specimens are from caterpillars that have been raised on leaves of its host plant.

How Do Butterflies Get Their Colors?

The scales are responsible for the bright coloration and patterns on the wings. Most scales contain colored pigments. The epidermal cells secrete the pigments into the cuticle that forms the scales.

Some scales reflect light to create color without pigments. Color that is due to reflected light (and not pigments) is called "iridescence." Iridescent scales reflect only some wavelengths (colors) of light but not others. A flat surface will reflect all wavelengths of light equally. However, surfaces with "micro-ridges," which are the same distance apart as the light waves, will interfere with reflection of some colors. Morpho butterfly wings are iridescent blue because the blue is reflected while longer wavelengths (green and red) are cancelled by interference.

Why are Butterflies Brightly Colored?

Butterflies use color patterns to find and attract mates. In many species, males and females have differences in color pattern known as sexual dimorphism. Additionally, males and females can have different flight behaviors that make it possible to identify male and females of some species from a distance.

Aposematism. Many butterflies are toxic to birds and advertise their toxicity with warning coloration (aposematism). Warning colors are typically some combination of black with red yellow or orange. Birds that eat a toxic insect will remember the color and pattern and refuse to eat insects with similar coloration. Many of the brightly colored butterflies are toxic to birds. However, it is not uncommon to collect butterflies and moths with wing damage indicative of bird attack. (Typically, a piece of the wing in the shape of a bird beak will be missing from an attacked butterfly or moth.) Moths that are not toxic to birds can avoid predation with a protective coloration to hide them during the day and by flying at night when most birds are not active.

Disruptive coloration. On some butterflies a different color pattern on the upper and lower wings can disrupt the ability of birds to follow butterflies in flight. The Morpho butterflies reflect a flash of light when the wings are held at the appropriate angle. The flash disappears when the wings close. This makes it difficult for predators to track the butterfly. Some butterflies like the mourning cloak and the coma have bright colors on the upper wings. If disturbed, they fold their wings so only the lower surface can be seen. When resting on the ground they can resemble dead leaves.

Butterflies as a hobby. Because of their bright and showy colors, butterflies are among the most popular insects for collectors and observers. Many localities have "butterfly counts" to count and observe butterfly species and numbers. Purdue University sponsors an annual butterfly count each July.

All modern adult Lepidoptera have mouthparts that form a long sucking tube for drinking nectar from flowers. Butterflies and moths are important pollinators of many plants. Some plants are better sources of nectar than others. Some plants may evolve a relationship with a single species of lepidopteran pollinator. For example, the plant nicotiana has flowers that only open at night. These flowers are pollinated by hawk moths that fly at night.

Why Do Butterflies Puddle?

Puddling is a behavior that is common in male butterflies. After a rain, salt present in the soil will dissolve into the water of puddles. As water evaporates, salt concentrates. By drinking the water, the butterflies collect salt. This behavior is necessary because caterpillars do not get enough salt (sodium) from eating plants. Salt is transferred to females during mating. Females use the salt to provision the eggs.

What Do Caterpillars Eat?

Lepidopteran larvae are called caterpillars. All caterpillars have chewing mouthparts. With a few exceptions, caterpillars feed on living plants. Caterpillars typically specialize by feeding only on parts of a plant such as foliage, flowers, seeds, or stems of plants including trees.

Butterfly caterpillars are picky eaters. Often, only one or a few species of plant are suitable food. The well-known Monarch Butterfly eats milkweed leaves. The Tiger Swallowtail caterpillars primarily feed on leaves of the tulip tree. If the host plants are not present, the butterflies will not be present. A common complaint of homeowners is the absence of butterflies in their yard and gardens. New subdivisions with mostly grassy lawn and no caterpillar host plants will not produce butterflies. People who like butterflies need to provide adequate food and habitat.

Caterpillar Adaptations

Caterpillars have a small head, a small thorax with tiny walking legs and a large abdomen. Adults lay eggs on the host plants, and the caterpillars often do not leave the plant. Thus, caterpillars do not need long legs. Most of the inside of a caterpillar is gut. The large gut in the abdomen processes food. Caterpillars spend most of their time feeding and may grow at a rapid rate. The fast rate of growth allows some Lepidoptera to have several generations per year.

How Do Caterpillars Move?

Many caterpillars have protuberances of the abdomen called pro-legs. The pro-legs support the abdomen and are used to grip the plant surface. Most caterpillars crawl by alternating contraction of their segments, planting the end of the abdomen and then pushing the front of the caterpillar forward.

Some caterpillars move instead by making a loop with the center of their body and are called "loopers" or "inchworms." The looping movement is only possible for caterpillars with a relatively thin abdomen that is flexible enough to bend. The "inchworm measuring the marigolds" in the song, *Inchworm,* is a caterpillar.

A few caterpillars like those of the gypsy moth will hang from trees by a silk thread. The wind can catch them and transport them a short distance.

What Are Important Enemies of Caterpillars?

Birds and small mammals such as mice are important predators of caterpillars. Caterpillars are food for predatory insects such as stink bugs, tiger beetles, ants, and wasps. Other enemies include parasitoids that develop inside or attached to the caterpillar.

How Do Caterpillars Defend Themselves?

Some caterpillars may have protective coloration that allows them to blend into their surroundings. Other caterpillars mimic animals or objects. For instance, some of the swallowtail caterpillars mimic snakes or bird droppings. These strategies are most effective against vertebrate predators that use their keen vision to locate prey. Visual disguises are less effective against insect predators that search by odor or touch.

Some caterpillars sequester toxins from plants or manufacture poisons or irritants. These caterpillars often have warning coloration. Warning coloration is typically black with red or yellow. Caterpillars of the swallowtail butterflies have a gland in the head that secretes butyric acid. This toxic secretion deters ants and other predators. Some caterpillars are protected by spines or irritating hairs that keep predators and parasitoids at bay.

How Do Adult Butterflies and Moths Defend Themselves?

Adult Lepidoptera that fly during the day either fool or poison enemies. Butterflies such as the (unrelated) Monarch and Viceroy butterflies have similar orange and black markings and both are toxic to birds. Birds that become ill after ingesting either will from then on avoid eating both. The black and yellow Pipevine Swallowtail is also toxic to predators. Numerous Swallowtail butterflies that are nontoxic "mimic" the coloration of the toxic Pipevine Swallowtail. Birds that learn to avoid the toxic Pipevine Swallowtail will also avoid its non-toxic mimics.

Mimicry

The clearwing moths mimic wasps. They fly during the day and have clear wings with black and yellow or black and red color warning patterns. At first glance they appear to be large wasps, but they are harmless and do not sting. Birds that learn to avoid stinging wasps will also avoid these moths.

Can Moths Hear?

Bats are important predators of many moths. Some moths can detect bat sonar. These moths will dive to the ground or initiate other bat avoidance flights if they detect bat sonar.

How Do Moths Find Mates?

Male moths typically find females by pheromone odor communication. Females release an odor (pheromone) that males use to locate the female. Some male moths are capable traveling long distances (up to 1 kilometer) to find a mate.

Butterflies communicate visually. The bright patterns on the wings are important in mate identification. Males patrol a location and are often territorial. Butterfly mating often occurs in the air and the flight is an important component of the courtship. For this reason, many butterfly species will not mate in captivity if confined to small containers. The confinement does not allow for enough room for the courtship behavior that is a prelude to mating.

Endangered Species

Several species of butterflies are endangered. The Karner Blue, found in Northwest Indiana is an endangered species. The Karner Blue is protected from collectors (it is illegal to collect Karner Blue butterflies) and its habitat is protected from land developers. Loss of habitat is the primary cause of extinction for insects. The Karner Blue feeds on lupine plants that are restricted in distribution. In order for the Karner Blue to survive, habitat that supports the lupine must be maintained. Interestingly, the Karner Blue caterpillars have a mutualistic relationship with ants. The Karner Blue secretes a sugary food for ants. The ants protect the caterpillars from their enemies. Areas that contain all the resources necessary to support the Karner Blue are limited. Destruction of the small areas of remaining habitat would cause its extinction.

What Are Butterfly Gardens?

People who enjoy butterflies may plant butterfly gardens to attract butterflies to their homes. Butterfly gardens contain plants that produce nectar that is used by adult butterflies. Good plants for attracting butterflies include butterfly weed (a kind of milkweed) and thistles. In the spring, the John Purdue Mall has flowers that attract many butterflies. Those who would like to create a butterfly garden can find many helpful resources. Purdue FNR has information on butterfly gardens at: http://www.ces.purdue.edu/extmedia/FNR/FNR-248-W.pdf

Important Lepidoptera

Many of the most damaging agricultural pests are caterpillars.

Corn Borer

The corn borer caterpillars bore into the stalks of corn. Corn borers rob the corn plant of nutrients and decrease corn yields. Corn borers can weaken stalks and cause them to break. In the summer large flights of corn borer moths fly over roadways next to corn fields at dusk. This makes quite a mess on the windshields of passing cars.

Corn Earworm

The corn earworm is a caterpillar that lives in the ears of corn. If you husk sweet corn and find a "worm" eating the kernels, it is probably a corn earworm caterpillar.

Armyworms are pests of numerous vegetable and field crops. Armyworms get their name because caterpillars that have consumed a field will migrate as "armies" of caterpillars to new fields. In outbreak years thousands of caterpillars migrate out of fields and cross roads and highways in search of food.

Tent Caterpillars

Larvae of tent caterpillars are common pests of ornamental trees, especially flowering crab apple trees. The female moth lays eggs in a single mass on the branches of a tree. The larvae are social. They live in a single "nest" that they make collectively by tying branches together with silk threads. This creates a web or "tent" around the caterpillars. The tent deters birds and other predators from eating the caterpillars. The caterpillars retreat to their nest during the day. At night the caterpillars leave the nest and feed on leaves. Tent caterpillars can defoliate branches and are unsightly, but typically, they do not cause long-term damage to the tree. Scraping the nest off the branches eliminates the nest. Dipping the nest in soapy water kills the caterpillars. Gloves are recommended because the hairs on the tent caterpillars can be irritating.

Gypsy Moth

Gypsy moth is an important invasive forest pest. Large populations of gypsy moth caterpillars can strip all the leaves off deciduous trees making the forest look like midwinter in July. The gypsy moth is a nuisance to homeowners because it can stress the trees. Large caterpillars produce copious amounts of frass. A large infestation of gyspy moth larvae can produce a constant "rain" of frass from large trees. Homeowners with large trees shading their patio may find outdoor barbeques a challenge during an outbreak.

How did gypsy moth reach the United States? A man named Trouvelot who was trying to create a silk industry in North America brought gypsy moth to Massachusetts in the 1800s. He tried to cross gypsy

Selected Lepidoptera

A. Caterpillars have a head and thorax that are relatively small compared to the abdomen. Note the 3 thoracic legs. The abdomen has protuberances called prolegs that support the abdomen and aid in locomotion.   B. There are several ways that caterpillars defend against predators. The hornworm has a sharp abdominal spine and white stripes that break up the outline of the caterpillar and help disguise it in the foliage.   C. Caterpillars of the white-marked tussock moth have hairs that cause irritation and bright markings to advertise the hazard to potential predators.   D. Smartweed caterpillar has "stinging" spines.   E. Caterpillar mimics a catkin.   F. Tent caterpillars build a nest with silk webbing to deter birds and other predators. The caterpillars feed at night and retreat inside their nest during the day.   G. Chrysalis (pupa

(continued on page 113)

Chapter 9 • Notable Groups of Insects

moths with silkworms (will not happen; they are unrelated species) but some gypsy moths escaped. Early attempts to eradicate the pest failed. For years, gypsy moths were confined to New England. Females are flightless so the insect must move by larvae blown by the wind or transportation of eggs.

How do gypsy moths move? Gypsy moths move large distances when their eggs are laid on firewood or on camping equipment in infested forests. Humans inadvertently transported gypsy moth to states neighboring Massachusetts and into Michigan in the 1970s. Gypsy moths are currently in the Northeast corner of Indiana but are not yet established in most of the state. Eventually a high-density population is expected to establish in Indiana from a large, permanent population that is slowly moving westward through Ohio.

How are gypsy moths detected? Isolated infestations can be eradicated using pheromones to prevent mating. Indiana has a "slow the spread" program that depends on using pheromones to monitor new infestations and eradicate small isolated populations. Monitoring is accomplished by a grid of pheromone traps; these are set up in each square mile. If gypsy moths have been transported into an area, male moths will be captured in the pheromone trap.

How are new infestations eliminated? New infestations of gypsy moth can be eliminated with pheromones. Tiny pheromone dispensers can be distributed throughout the infestation area. The dispensers far outnumber the female moths. The male moths spend all their time finding dispensers and trying to mate with them. Female moths are unable to compete with more numerous pheromone dispensers and fail to mate. The population is eliminated because no female moth produces fertile eggs.

Clothes Moth

Clothes moth caterpillars feed on wool, which primarily consists of the protein, keratin. Clothes moths do not eat synthetic fabrics. Replacement of wool with synthetics has reduced the clothes moth problem. The caterpillars require proteins to survive and synthetics do not provide adequate nutrition. Clothes moths caterpillars are known for their water retention. All their water must come from the digestion of wool. Storing woolens in cedar chests or in containers with mothballs can prevent clothes moth damage. Both the cedar and the mothballs are insecticidal.

Silkworm

Silk is the second most important insect product after honey. Silk is a protein produced by the silk glands of caterpillars. Commercial silk is collected from the silkworm pupae. Before pupation, the silkworm caterpillar spins a single silk strand that surrounds the pupa. Moths cannot be allowed to emerge from the pupa because they break the silk. Steaming the cocoons kills the pupa. After steaming, the cocoons are dried and can be stored. The cocoons are soaked in hot water to release the silk strands. The strands are wound onto spools and spun into thread. Thread can be used to make a fine cloth. Silk cloth is a fine fabric that is light, strong, and dyes well. Silk fabric holds its form during washing.

(plate caption *continued*)

stage) of the monarch butterfly   H. A bagworm is the cocoon of the bagworm moth.   I. A moth feeds on oozing sap at night.   J. Indian meal moth is a common pest of stored foods.   K. Tobacco hornworm moth   L. A Tiger Swallowtail butterfly collects nectar from a flower.   M. A Painted Lady butterfly drinks nectar through its coiled mouthparts (proboscis). Note the knobs on the ends of the antennae that are present on all butterflies.

Silk production was invented over 4,000 years ago in China. Silk production was a local secret until AD 550, when silkworms and the trade secrets of silk production were brought to Constantinople.

Silkworm is a completely domesticated species that does not thrive in nature. Cocoon production is often a cottage industry. Caterpillars are fed leaves of the mulberry tree. Caterpillars and leaves are kept on large woven mats that support the caterpillars but allow the frass to drop through the cracks. Fresh leaves are picked from trees and placed on the mats daily. Children often care for the caterpillars. The cocoons are sold at markets. Silk production is an important source of household income in many parts of Asia.

Flies, Fleas, and Carriers of Disease

The flies or **Diptera (Di = two; ptera = wings)** are one of the four largest groups of insects. Well over 100,000 species have been described. The fore wings are true wings, but the hind wings of adults are highly modified as knob-like structures known as *halteres*. The two fore wings provide lift and movement through the air. The halteres vibrate during flight. Their gyroscopic action can aid in turning and balancing. Halteres allow flies to make acrobatic maneuvers in the air. Although some Diptera are clunky fliers, many flies (such as the common house fly) are noted for their agility, rapid acceleration and quick takeoffs.

What Is the Life Cycle of Diptera?

Diptera have complete metamorphosis, an egg, larva, pupa, and adult stage. The larvae of flies are legless. Many larvae are worm-like and called maggots. The pupa often forms inside the cuticle of the final larva stage.

How Ancient are the Diptera?

The Diptera first appear in the fossil record in the Triassic period over 200 million years ago. The Triassic period begins with the extinction event 250 millions of years ago (mya) that caused extinction of 70 percent of all terrestrial species. The Diptera were one of the insect groups that thrived and diversified in the Triassic, the same period when the early dinosaurs evolved.

What Is the Most Important Group of Diptera to Human Health?

Mosquitoes are important vectors of human diseases. Diseases transmitted by mosquitoes include: malaria, West Nile virus, yellow fever, encephalitis, and elephantiasis. These diseases are only transmitted by the adult female mosquitoes.

How Do Mosquitoes Transmit Disease?

Diseases are transmitted by mosquitoes during blood feeding. Mosquitoes have tubular mouthparts that they insert through the skin. The ends of the mouthparts have tiny saw-like teeth that can saw through the skin and through a blood vessel. Mosquitoes secrete saliva that prevents the blood from clotting and plugging the mouthparts. Diseases that are transmitted (**vectored**) by mosquitoes are contained in the mosquito saliva and are injected into the host during feeding.

How Do Mosquitoes Acquire Diseases?

If a mosquito bites a host that is infected with a disease, the disease pathogen will be ingested by the mosquito along with the blood meal. In order for the pathogen to be transmitted to a new host, it must leave the mosquito gut and move to the salivary glands. Pathogens that cannot leave the gut in order to move to the salivary glands are not transmitted by mosquitoes. This is why pathogens such as the AIDS virus are NOT transmitted by mosquitoes. Some diseases can reproduce in the mosquito as well as in vertebrate hosts. Reproduction in the mosquito increases the rate of transmission.

What Causes Mosquito Bites?

Mosquito saliva contains proteins and other factors that prevent blood from clotting. When the female is finished feeding some of the protein is left behind. Mosquito proteins can trigger the cells of the human immune system to aggregate at the site to remove the foreign protein. It is the reaction of our immune system that causes the mosquito bite.

Why do mosquitoes bite? In order to produce eggs, female mosquitoes must take a blood meal. Blood has many nutrients that female mosquitoes process to provision their eggs. Only the female mosquitoes take a blood meal. Male mosquitoes feed on nectar. The mosquito larvae feed on detritus that is deficient in protein. Blood contains substantial protein and compensates for the deficient larval diet.

Where Do Mosquito Larvae Live?

Female mosquitoes lay eggs in water or in areas that are prone to flooding or ponding. Some eggs can withstand dry spells. After a rain, small pools of water can form. Mosquito eggs swell and hatch. It takes about 2 weeks to go from egg to adult. This is why adult mosquito populations often increase about two weeks after a rain.

What Do Mosquito Larvae Do?

Mosquito larvae, called "wrigglers," are aquatic. The wrigglers make jerky undulations to move through the water. The larvae feed on small plants and aquatic organisms. Larvae can hold enough oxygen for long dives, but must go to the surface to breathe air. Larvae break the surface of the water with a posterior breathing tube. The tube has water-repellent hairs at the end that keep water out of the tube. Mosquito larvae can be suffocated by coating the surface of water with oils or chemicals that cover the breathing tube. Another method of mosquito control is to eliminate standing water where mosquito larvae develop.

What Is The Most Important Mosquito Disease?

Malaria is the number one disease transmitted by mosquitoes worldwide. There are 300 to 500 million cases of malaria per year including 2 to 3 million deaths. Over 1 million of those deaths are children. In some parts of Africa as many as 40 percent of all toddlers may die of malaria.

What Is Malaria?

Malaria is a plasmodium, a type of single-cell organism. In humans, the malaria plasmodium infects the liver and red blood cells. The malaria destroys blood cells causing anemia. Malaria also causes a high fever. Only part of the life cycle takes place in humans. The other part of the malaria life cycle occurs in mosquitoes.

Is there a Vaccine or Cure?

Some drugs have limited effectiveness against malaria, but there is no permanent cure. Vaccines have not been successful because the malaria parasite mutates rapidly. Recently, more intensive measures to research and control malaria have been initiated, including millions of dollars donated by private foundations.

Is there Malaria in the United States?

Malaria was prevalent in the United States in the 1800s including Indiana. Malaria was eliminated from large parts of North America by "draining the swamps." Drainage tiles were installed across large tracts of land and are operational in much of Indiana today. Malaria was eliminated from the United States in the twentieth century by improved sanitation, the use of window screens and pesticides. These strategies reduced the pool of malaria in the U.S. population. Today, there is little malaria to transmit in the United States even though mosquito vectors are still present. Malaria is a human disease that is primarily transmitted by mosquitoes that specialize on biting humans

Why Is DDT Still Used Against Malaria?

Malaria transmission can be reduced by the use of the insecticide DDT. DDT use worldwide was discontinued because of environmental contamination. DDT is banned from use in the United States to prevent environmental contamination. However, DDT use has been revived in some malaria hot spots because DDT is inexpensive, relatively safe to humans and effective. If DDT is strictly limited to indoor use only, environmental problems can be avoided. The use of DDT is controversial, but has recently been revived in some areas. In these areas, the health risk from exposure to DDT is small compared to the devastating health consequences of malaria.

What Animals Do Mosquitoes Bite?

Some mosquitoes will feed on the blood of many species of animals including humans, mammals, birds, and reptiles. Mosquitoes that feed on birds and humans can transfer viruses and other pathogens from birds to humans. Some important viruses transmitted by mosquitoes, such as West Nile Virus and encephalitis, are primarily bird viruses. Over evolutionary time, pathogens that are endemic in an animal population will become less virulent and animals will become more tolerant or resistant. The pathogens become widespread in the host animal populations. However, these pathogens can be virulent if transferred to other species. In humans, bird viruses can cause high fever and even death.

What Is West Nile Virus?

West Nile Virus is a disease that moved from Africa to North America in the late 1990s. West Nile Virus is well established in North American bird populations including bird populations in Indiana. There have been several hospitalizations and deaths from West Nile Virus in Indiana and the Lafayette area. West Nile Virus is most dangerous to people who have weak immune systems including some of the very young and elderly. West Nile may cause milder infections in many people that go unreported.

How Is West Nile Virus Controlled?

Because West Nile is primarily a bird virus, transmission can be reduced by control of mosquitoes that bite both humans and birds. West Nile is commonly transmitted by species of *Culex* mosquitoes.

Culex mosquitoes develop in small pools of stagnant water, including drain gutters, old tires, cans, and other garbage. Good sanitation can eliminate breeding sites.

Weather can also affect West Nile incidence. In 2006, eighty cases of West Nile and five fatalities were reported in Indiana. In 2007, a dry or drought year, only seven cases of West Nile were reported in Indiana through mid-September (one fatality). West Nile Virus incidence in the bird population can be monitored, especially by testing dead birds. If many dead birds test positive for West Nile Virus, more intensive mosquito control measures will be used.

What Is Encephallitis?

Encephallitis is primarily a bird virus that can cause high fevers in humans. In the late 1960s, an outbreak of St Louis encephalitis led Indiana to establish a mosquito monitoring and control program. Encephalitis causes a high fever that can lead to brain damage. The mosquito control program for encephalitis is also effective against West Nile Virus. Much of the government infrastructure necessary to limit the spread of West Nile Virus was already in place before it reached Indiana.

What Is Yellow Fever?

Yellow fever is a viral disease found in South and Central America. In the 1800s, high incidence of yellow fever among workers prevented the French from completing the Panama Canal. The United States took over the project and completed the project. A U.S. Army surgeon, Dr Walter Reed, did pioneering work on the transmission of yellow fever by mosquitoes. His team proved that mosquitoes transmitted yellow fever. Some of his researchers died of yellow fever in the course of their research. This was the first demonstration that mosquitoes could transmit disease. The research led to mosquito control projects and use of mosquito netting to protect workers reduced the disease incidence. Today, a yellow fever vaccine is available. Yellow fever cannot be eliminated because monkeys are a reservoir for the virus. It is impossible to vaccinate all the monkeys or otherwise eliminate the yellow fever virus from the monkey population.

How Are Mosquitoes Controlled?

Mosquito larvae are the targets of most **control** efforts. Mosquito control involves elimination of breeding areas, treating mosquito-breeding areas with control agents and in some cases fogging adults with pesticides. Fogging adults is the least effective strategy. Control agents for mosquito larvae include some pesticides, analogs of juvenile hormone that prevent mosquito larvae from becoming adults and water surface treatments (surfactants and oils) that suffocate mosquito larvae that must come to the surface to breathe.

What Is Leishmaniasis?

Leishmaniasis is a protozoan disease transmitted by sand flies. Leishmaniasis is common in the Arabian peninsula and Iraq. Well over 500 U.S. soldiers have contracted leishmaniasis in Iraq since 2003. The soldiers call it the "Baghdad boil." Prevalence of Leishmaniasis in Afghanistan is high. In 2002, the World Health Organization estimated that over 200,000 were infected in Kabul alone. Leishmaniasis appears as a necrotic region on the skin. Symptoms may take up to 6 months to appear. Leishmaniasis is easily treated by physicians. Failure to treat can lead to problems with the immune system and disfiguration.

What Is Elephantiasis?

Elephantiasis is a parasitic worm that is transmitted by mosquitoes. The worm invades the lymphatic system and blocks fluid removal from the limbs. This causes the infected limb to swell to elephantine proportions (thus the name). In rare cases, the parasites infect the male scrotum and can cause expansive swelling. Elephantiasis can be treated by drugs that kill the worms.

What Is Lyme Disease?

Lyme disease is primarily transmitted by the deer tick, and to a lesser extent by deer flies. Lyme disease is caused by bacteria. In about one third of cases, a bull's eye rash appears at the site of the bite. In many cases, Lyme disease is misdiagnosed or undiagnosed. Lyme disease can cause joint pain and joint inflammation. In one notable case, the quarterback of Florida State University was found on the street disoriented, disheveled, and incoherent. He was diagnosed with severe advanced Lyme disease that had caused some swelling of the brain. He was treated with antibiotics that cured the bacterial infection, but subsequently missed the entire 2005 football season.

What Do House Flies Do?

The house fly is a common nuisance. The flies lay eggs in decaying food. The larvae are maggots that develop rapidly. House flies are noted for their quick take-off and landing and ability to avoid capture. House flies have taste receptors in their feet. They taste the food as they walk on it. House flies are noted for their ability to walk on walls and ceilings. Their ability to walk upside down depends on tiny hairs on their feet. The hairs produce tiny droplets of liquid that "stick" the fly to the ceiling.

How Do Flies Land On the Ceiling?

Landing on ceilings is tricky. Flies cannot fly upside down or do a barrel roll to land on the ceiling. Instead, they fly very close to the ceiling, grasp the ceiling by extending their front legs over their head and back flip onto the ceiling,

Important Flies That Do Not Vector Human Disease

What Are Apple Maggots?

Apple maggots are pests of apples. Female apple maggots lay eggs on the outside of apples. The maggot hatches and tunnels into the apple to complete development. The fully developed apple maggot leaves the apple and pupates in the soil. Apple maggot pupae can over winter in soil and adults emerge in summer when apples are present.

In fresh apples, the maggot damage can be cut out and the rest of the apple is good to eat.

> Q. What is worse than finding a maggot in an apple?
> A. Finding half of a maggot.

Apple maggots open the apple to colonization by fungi. Fungi can spread from one rotten apple to the other apples in storage. This gives rise to the saying, "One rotten apple spoils the barrel." Most commercial apples in the United States are placed in cool storage and marketed throughout the year. Apple maggots damage can cause apples to rot in storage.

What Are Hessian Flies?

Hessian flies are a pest of wheat. Hessian flies were first brought into the United States in the bedding of Hessian soldiers during the Revolutionary War. The larvae feed on wheat plants and stunt their growth. Purdue University hosts a major research effort by the USDA to control the Hessian fly.

What Are Leaf Miners?

Some fly larvae develop between the upper and lower surfaces of leaves. The larvae create tunnels inside the leaf that are visible from the outside. Not all leaf mines are made by fly larvae. Larvae of some wasps, beetles and caterpillars can mine leaves.

What Are Gall Flies?

Gall flies develop inside plant stems. Gall flies alter the plant structure so the plant forms a protective shell around the insect and provides the insect with food and protection from predators. Gall flies have a special saliva that causes the plant to make the gall.

How Are Flies Used in Crime Investigations?

Blow flies are attracted to dead bodies and are often the first insects to arrive on the scene. Blow fly maggots develop at a consistent rate that is dependent on temperature. Crime investigators can accurately estimate time of death by having a temperature record and knowing blow fly development.

What Are the Most Important Fly Pollinators?

Hover flies are important pollinators of flowers. Hover flies mimic bees and wasps. Birds and other potential predators avoid them. They look dangerous, as if they might inflict a painful sting. They are harmless.

Why Are Fruit Flies Used In Genetics?

Fruit flies have been very important in the study of genetics. Fruit flies have a genetic system that is similar to humans. Fruit flies have a complete generation in 2 weeks. Twenty-six generations of fruit flies can be studied in 1 year. Progress with animals that produce only one generation per year is much slower (twenty-six times slower). Fruit flies contain "polytene" chromosomes in their salivary glands. Instead of a single copy of the DNA, salivary chromosomes may contain hundreds of copies. This allowed scientists to study the structure of the chromosomes themselves.

The fruit fly was one of the first animals to have its complete genome sequenced. We now have the complete genetic code contained by the fruit fly DNA. Many fruit fly genes have counterparts in humans (all life on earth is related). We can learn about human genes by studying analogs in fruit flies.

What Are Crane Flies?

Crane flies are large flies that resemble mosquitoes, are attracted to lights and commonly found indoors. Sometimes, they are mistaken for giant mosquitoes, but they do not bite.

Flies in Summary

Many flies are **pests**. They vector diseases. They can be nuisance biters. They can harm livestock. They can damage our food crops.

Other flies are beneficial. They pollinate plants. They recycle waste. They decompose dead animals.

Fleas

Fleas are most closely related to flies, but are placed in their own Order, Siphonaptera. "Siphonaptera" is derived from the Greek "siphon" meaning tube or pipe and "aptera" meaning wingless.

Cat Fleas

The cat flea is the number one veterinarian problem in both dogs and cats. Cat fleas infest a variety of mammals including common feral animals such as raccoons, opossums, and squirrels. These feral animals serve as a reservoir of fleas that can transfer to a pet when it is outside.

Flea adults feed on blood and excrete excess nutrients (derived from the blood) that fall to the ground or the nest of the host. Flea eggs also fall off the host into a nest or onto the ground. Cat flea larvae develop off the host, feeding on the droppings from the adults. The larvae pupate and emerge as adults off the host. Newly emerged adult fleas are inactive until they sense a potential host. Hosts are detected by temperature. If the air around the flea warms, it will become active and leap into the air and onto its host.

Flea treatment. A variety of insecticides and formulations are used for treatment of fleas. Flea shampoo is insecticide that is formulated as a soapy product that can be used to coat a cat or dog. When applying flea shampoo, always wear gloves, because it is an insecticide. Owners of poodle salons have reported insecticide-poisoning symptoms from overexposure to flea shampoo. Most commonly this occurs from using flea shampoo without gloves.

Flea Collars

Flea collars are marginally effective for flea control. They are most effective in the area of the head but are progressively less effective at larger distances. Flea collars should NEVER be used on people. Some soldiers in Iraq tried wrapping flea collars around their legs to deter biting flies, instead of the safe and approved insect repellent. The wax in the flea collars melted in the heat and caused severe skin damage. NEVER use any insect control product in a manner that is not listed on the label directions.

Severe flea infestations are usually treated with systemic flea insecticides given orally to the dog or cat (sometimes placed topically on the head). Severe infestations can lead to flea allergies that produce scabby skin on the pet. NEVER use a flea treatment formulated for a dog on a cat. Cats are far more sensitive to most insecticides than dogs. A dose tolerated by a dog may kill a cat.

Rat Fleas

Rat fleas are primarily parasites of rats. However, rat flea adults will occasionally move off the host and onto another host. Rat fleas are capable of spreading diseases from rats to humans and other animals. Rat fleas have greatly influenced human history through the transmission of bubonic plague (Black Death). Bubonic plague is carried by rats and transmitted to humans by rat fleas that feed on rats then subsequently bite humans. (Note: Cat fleas do NOT transmit plague.)

Insect Diseases and History

Insects as vectors of diseases have had a major impact on human history. Not all plagues, (for example the influenza pandemic of 1918) require an insect vector. However, malaria, transmitted by mosquitoes, has altered human evolution. The bubonic plague, a disease transmitted by the rat flea, has had enormous geopolitical impacts, leading to the collapse of entire civilizations and overturning established political world order.

Plague

Plague is caused by a bacterium, *Yersinia pestis*. Its reservoir is the Indian rat flea, *Xenopsylla cheopsis*. The Indian rat flea can survive for 6 to 12 months off a host in dung, an abandoned rodent's nest, or textile bales. Rat fleas can live on many rodent species, including rats, squirrels, and mice. Infected, rats are often asymptomatic until near death. The fleas leave the dying rats and seek new hosts. Fleas can transfer the plague bacterium to people (if nearby) through feeding on human blood, even though humans do not serve as a primary host. Rat control is an important aspect of controlling plague.

Bubonic plague is named for the symptoms it causes in people, swelling of the lymph nodes called buboes. Lymph nodes in the armpits and groin become very tender and swollen (1 to 10 cm diameter) 1 to 6 days after infection with *Yersinia pestis*. The golf-ball-sized buboes are painful and can discharge fetid pus. In some cases the bacterium invades the lungs and can be transmitted by coughing.

Individuals that are resistant to plague will run a high fever, survive, and be immune as a result of exposure. In susceptible individuals, the bacterium invades the blood and the victim dies of septicemia. A typical victim dies within 7 days of infection.

The Black Death and the Collapse of the Mongol Empire
By 1300, the Mongols controlled a trading empire that stretched across Asia to eastern Europe. The Mongols were the consummate "free traders" who created wealth by trading goods among areas of the globe. The Mongols unified the trade routes across Asia and maintained roads and accommodations to facilitate trade. In a relatively short period during the 1330s, the Mongol empire collapsed.

As is discussed in the chapter on invasive species, movement of goods through trade can also transport unwanted biological organisms. The organism that caused the downfall of the Mongol empire was an extremely virulent form of bubonic plague. Between 1328 and 1332, the leadership changed many times as members of the ruling family died of the plague. In 1331, about 90 percent of the residents of Hopei Province (now in China) had died. By 1351, between one half and two thirds of the population of what is now China died of the plague. The plague spread along the trading routes carried by fleas and rats harboring in the trade goods. Within a few years, the network of trading stations along the trade routes collapsed and the major regions of the Mongol Empire lost much of the ability to communicate and trade goods. Since their power was built

A. Goldenrod gall. A fly larva develops inside the plant stem and alters causes the plant to grow a gall to provide food and shelter. The larva will pupate inside the gall and an adult will emerge in spring.   B. Fly collecting nectar and pollen from a flower   C. Hover flies are important pollinators of plants. Even though they are harmless and do not sting, most predators avoid them because their coloration resembles bees and wasps that do sting.   D. A flea comb can be used to manually remove fleas from your pet.   E. A cat suffering from dermatitis cause by flea allergy.   F. Top row from left: Bee eggs, larva, pupa and abdomen of honey bee worker showing bees wax scales.

(*continued on page 123*)

Chapter 9 • Notable Groups of Insects

on their ability to deliver trade goods, between regions, the empire soon collapsed and split into disconnected regions.

The plague was carried to Europe and Africa by ship and reached the islands of Greenland and Iceland. Over the remainder of the fourteenth century, the world population declined between 10 and 20 percent due to the plague.

The plague continued to ravage Europe, Asia, and Africa for several centuries. Over time, the exposed populations developed resistance to the plague and the disease became less virulent.

The Plague in North America

During the 1300s, the Americas were spared the effects of the plague because trade between the Americas and Europe was non-existent. The increase in trade after 1492 would eventually bring the plague to North America.

In the early 1600s in the years just prior to the landing of the Pilgrims in Plymouth, Massachusetts in 1620, a devastating plague had killed many of the Native American inhabitants of the region. There is evidence to suggest that the plague was a form of bubonic plague, perhaps carried by rats and their fleas leaving fishing ships that sailed into rivers to collect fresh water.

The Native Americans had no past exposure to the plague and there was little resistance in the population. It is estimated that between 90 percent and 96 percent of the population of Southern New England died during the plague. Villages were abandoned as all or all but a few residents perished. Those not killed immediately would move to other villages and spread the plague.

The plague meant that the Pilgrims found empty villages and abandoned fields already cleared for agriculture. The population of Native Americans was so depressed that they could offer little resistance to colonization of the land by the Pilgrims and other Europeans that followed. The plague in North America was an important geopolitical event that changed the course of history in North America.

Lessons of the Past

These accounts of plagues past should serve as precautionary tales. Societies are still vulnerable to new plagues. Preventing them requires vigilance and proper application of modern science and medicine. Plagues of the twentieth century have included influenza and HIV epidemics that have killed millions of people. Diseases such as H1N1 (or bird flu) or ebola have the potential to become plagues should they become resistant to current control methods. Plagues require the confluence of numerous factors to take root. Fortunately, HIV-AIDs is not transmitted by

(plate caption *continued*)

Bottom row from left: Worker, Drone and Queen bee.   G. Bee keeper tools for working a hive: Gloves, bee brush, hive tools for prying apart frames and smoker for quieting the bees.   H. Bee hive with bee boxes that stack.   I. An open hive box showing the removable frames.   J. Frame removed from the hive. Honey bees build comb on the frames using bees wax. Eggs are laid in the some cells of the comb by the queen and bees are reared in those cells. Other cells are used for storing pollen and honey.

---

mosquitoes (not enough blood is exchanged and the virus does not live in the mosquito) or that epidemic could be far worse than it is. The lack of knowledge of how the bubonic plague was transmitted allowed the plague to spread unabated. Knowledge of the role of rat fleas could have led to measures to control both the rats and the fleas and lessen the impact of the plague. That was an earlier time that was not blessed with our current knowledge of diseases and their insect vectors. The ability to control insects capable of transmitting these diseases may be important for preventing the next plague.

Hymenoptera: The Sawflies and Wasps

Hymenoptera comes from the Latin meaning "membrane wing" (hymen = membrane, optera = wing). The wings of most Hymenoptera have areas that are thin and transparent like a membrane. In the absence of pigments, insect cuticle is transparent. Adult Hymenoptera have two pairs of membranous wings. The hind wings are typically smaller than the forewings and are coupled so they beat in unison during flight.

Hymenoptera is one of the four largest orders of insects with over 100,000 species. Like the other largest groups of insects, the Hymenoptera have complete metamorphosis—an egg, larva, pupa, and adult stage. The Hymenoptera include the familiar bees and ants that are specialized types of wasps.

Mouthparts

Most Hymenoptera have chewing mouthparts as larvae and as adults. Exceptions include adult honey bees that have mouthparts modified as tubes for sucking nectar.

Earliest Hymenoptera

The most ancient Hymenopteran fossils are over 200 million years old. Hymenoptera evolved after the Permian extinction 251 million years ago (mya). As a group they are more recent than beetles and flies. The earliest Hymenoptera ate plants and had larvae that resembled caterpillars. Modern representatives of the primitive plant feeding Hymenoptera include the sawflies. Sawfly larvae are often mistaken for caterpillars. Sawfly adults have thick bodies and lack the abdominal constriction present in the wasps.

Wasps

The largest group of Hymenoptera is the wasps. Wasps typically have venom glands in the abdomen and the tip of the abdomen is modified into a stinger. Wasps also have a constriction of the abdomen between the first and second segment. This constriction allows the abdomen to be flexible and the stinger to be directed. Wasps are able to contort their abdomen and use their stinger to inject venom into prey. Wasps that feed on plants may still retain their stinger and venom for protection against predators and nest intruders.

Abdominal flexibility enhances the ability of parasitoid wasps to lay eggs in hosts. Some parasitoids are able to bend the tip of their abdomen in front of their head to inject an egg into the host. The abdominal constriction most likely evolved in small parasitoids. The constriction has been maintained throughout the evolution of Hymenoptera and it contributes to the ability of large Hymenoptera to direct their stinger to vulnerable sites on prey or to attack intruders.

What Is Stinging?

An insect sting is defined as the injection of venom into another animal. Stings are delivered using a stinger, a modification of the ovipositor. Stings are distinct from insect bites, which are inflicted with the mouthparts. The stingers of Hymenoptera resemble miniature hypodermic needles. The tip is sharp for insertion into the target. The stinger is connected by a duct to a venom sac. When the stinger is inserted into an animal, the muscles of the venom sac contract and inject venom into the animal.

Hymenoptera are the only insects that sting. (Some caterpillars have irritating hairs but not a true sting. Other insects that mimic stinging Hymenoptera are harmless.) Hymenoptera will sting to defend their nest. The nest contains progeny and concentrated resources that must be guarded against predators or competitors that can enter the nest. Most wasps can sting multiple times. The wasp stinger is needle-like and can slip in and out of the skin. In contrast, the honey bee stinger has barbed hooks that cause the stinger to be left behind.

What Is a Venom?

The venoms are a mixture of chemicals, frequently containing proteins, which are used to immobilize prey or inflict pain on an intruder. Many wasps will use their venom for immobilizing prey but not for defense against predators.

However, venoms can be a powerful deterrent to predators and intruders among wasps that use venoms for defense. Most people have been stung by a wasp. The painful sting is memorable. One encounter is enough for most people to learn to not attempt to handle any insect with black and yellow warning markings. Stinging Hymenoptera often advertise with visible black and yellow stripes. The color pattern alone is protection against potential predators that have experienced a sting.

Parasitoids

The majority of wasps are tiny and develop inside living insects as parasitoids. Parasitoids utilize the nutrients present in other insects to grow and develop. A female parasitoid wasp will locate a suitable host and inject eggs and venom with her ovipositor. In some cases the host is paralyzed. In other cases, it continues to live and feed even as the parasitoids hatch and consume the host from the inside. The parasitoid larvae complete their larval and pupal molts within the host. The adults leave the host and seek other prey.

The largest family of parasitoid wasps, the ichneumons, contains over 80,000 species. There are parasitoids of eggs, larvae, pupae, and adult stages of other insects.

Some parasitoid adults can swim and lay their eggs on insects underwater. The size of the wasp depends on the size of the host. The fairy wasps are among the smallest known insects.

Parasitoids and Immunity

Insects are not defenseless against parasitoids. Some insect hemolymph cells are capable of recognizing and attacking parasitoids and other invaders. Thus, parasitoids may only be able to successfully defeat the immune system of one or a few insects that they exploit as hosts. The specialization of parasitoids has led to the large number of species.

Some parasitoids have a unique method of defeating the host insect immune system. They transmit viruses to their host that disables the host immune system. (An insect version of AIDS!) With the immune system disabled, the parasitoid can exploit the nutrients of the defenseless host. Parasitoids all inject their host with venom.

Parasitoids and Biological Control

Parasitoids can limit the growth of the population of their hosts. As the number of hosts increases, the number of parasitoids can also increase because hosts become easier to find. Parasitoids increase the mortality of the host and limit reproduction. In some cases, parasitoids can greatly limit the damage that pest insects cause to crops. These parasitoids may be an important component of biological insect control.

Common Wasps

Many of the larger wasps have high visibility and familiar common names such as hornet, mud dauber, yellow jacket, and cicada killer. Sometimes common names are applied to groups of familiar wasps such as "bees" and "ants."

Nests

Most of the larger wasps are protected in nests as larvae. Typically, the digestive systems of larvae in nests are not complete. Food enters but does not exit. This prevents the nest from becoming fouled. Waste is excreted by pupae just before they emerge as an adult.

Social Groups

The larva may be in an individual nest or part of a group nest. Many species of Hymenoptera are solitary but sociality is common in the Hymenoptera. Many different types of social organization are found within the Hymenoptera from simply sharing a nest location and its defense to elaborate caste systems of queens, workers, communal care of the young and overlapping generations of individuals within the same nest.

Cicada Killers

Commonly seen solitary wasps include the cicada killer, a frighteningly large wasp that lays its eggs in cicadas. Cicada killers look like they are large enough to deliver a deadly sting. However, they are not aggressive. People are almost never stung by them, unless they try to handle them or step on them. If stung, the venom is not deadly. Cicada killers can be observed at a respectful distance without risk of attack.

The cicada killer digs a nest in the ground, and then flies off to find prey. The cicada killer will sting a cicada with venom that immobilizes the cicada. The cicada killer files the cicada back to the nest. The cicada is placed at the bottom of the nest. An egg is laid on the cicada and the nest is closed. The cicada killer larva has plenty of food for development and is protected from predators and competitors.

Hornets

Hornets are common wasps that make characteristic nests in trees. Nests are made from wood that is chewed, partially digested, and regurgitated. The regurgitated material resembles paper.

Hornet colonies are small early in the year but become larger and more complex as the colony grows. The size of the nest is expanded to accommodate the growing population. Hornet nests can be quite large and visible when trees lose their leaves. However, these nests are fragile and need constant repair. Nests are destroyed by weather over the winter because there are no wasps to repair it.

Hornets capture prey (flies) to feed to young. The adults have a constricted abdomen and cannot digest large flies. Instead, adults feed flies to the larvae that do not have a constricted digestive system. The larvae process and digest the food. A portion of the food is regurgitated to feed the colony.

Carpenter Bees

Carpenter bees make nests in wood but do not eat wood. They can be detected by the wood dust they leave under the entrance to their nest. They can damage houses.

Mud Dauber

Not all nests are made from wood and paper. Mud dauber wasps gather mud to build their nests. Some mud daubers make nests of parallel mud tubes that resemble organ pipes. Organ pipe mud daubers are common in Indiana and often construct their nests on houses or other structures. Typical prey for mud daubers include spiders and caterpillars. Prey are immobilized with venom and placed in the cells of the nest. An egg is laid and the cell is sealed. The larvae develop without further parental care.

Yellow Jackets

Yellow jackets are wasps that make nests underground or inside cavities. Yellow jackets are especially aggressive in the fall. They forage intensely to collect enough food to survive the upcoming winter. Yellow jackets are frequently found entering cans of soda seeking sugar. Unsuspecting people may get stung on the mouth instead of a thirst quenching drink if they fail to notice the visitor in their can. Sometimes, people mistakenly call yellow jackets "bees" because they are similar in size and coloration to honey bees. However, yellow jackets have a smooth body. They lack the body hair found on honey bees. Yellow jackets are commonly found around human habitations. In Indiana, more people are stung by yellow jackets than any other type of bee or wasp. Many people who think they have been stung by a bee have actually been stung by a yellow jacket instead. It hurts all the same, but we should correctly identify the culprit so we address the correct problem. In Indiana yellow jackets are the most common wasp foragers at picnics where people eat food outdoors. In the fall, yellow jackets are common visitors to tailgate parties.

Honey Bees

What Are Bees?

Bees are a branch of the wasp family tree that includes several families. As a group, bees have a robust body and are noted for having many hairs. By comparison, the bodies of common wasps are smooth and hairless. About 25,000 described species of Hymenoptera are bees.

What Are Honey Bees?

The name "honey bee" is applied to about eight to ten species of bees in the genus *Apis*. Honey bees are social insects that live together in large colonies that are attended by bee keepers. The most common honey bee species in the United States is *Apis mellifera*.

What Do Honey Bees Eat?

Honey bees collect nectar and pollen from plants. They process the nectar and pollen to make honey and bee bread that they use as their food. Bees also need a source of water.

How Do Bees Collect Pollen?

Pollen attaches to the hairs of bees and is transported as bees fly from flower to flower gathering nectar. Flowers produce nectar as a "reward" to entice bees to visit. Flowers gain by having an efficient method of pollination. Bees also collect pollen for food. The hind legs of bees have special areas for collecting pollen called "pollen baskets." Pollen is high in protein and other nutrients. Pollen complements the diet of nectar, which is high in sugar.

How Valuable Is Bee Pollination?

Pollination is worth over $14 billion annually to growers. Up to one third of food crops are pollinated by honey bees. Migratory beekeepers are paid to transport their hives to fruit orchards (including almonds, peaches, pears, cherry, blueberries, and watermelons). Without bee pollination fruit set is reduced. Loss of bee colonies in 2007 greatly increased the price that growers must pay for pollination services.

What Is Honey?

Nectar from flowers is digested by bees and then regurgitated to form honey. The honey is stored in cells in the nest. Nectar contains chemicals produced by plants in addition to sugar. These plant chemicals can impart a flavor to the honey. The most common honey sold in U.S. stores is clover honey, which has a mild flavor. However, honey made from tree flowers such as basswood or orange blossom can have a stronger flavor.

How Do Bees Make a Nest?

Bees prefer to make their nests in a confined space. In nature, this is often a hollow tree. The bees will collect resin from trees to make propolis (bee glue) that they use to seal the cracks in the tree. Sealing the nest area is important for keeping predators out of the nest.

Inside the nest the bees make a honey comb. The comb is a series of wax cells that is used for storing honey and rearing young.

What Is Beeswax?

Some cells on the abdomens of worker bees secrete "beeswax" in the form of wax scales. The wax scales are chewed by worker bees and used to form the cells of the honey comb. The comb cells are hexagonal and closely packed. When cells are full of honey, they are capped shut with beeswax. Beeswax has a number of uses including candles and is the preferred wax for use in wax museums.

How Are Modern Bee Hives Constructed?

Modern bee hives consist of a series of boxes open on the top and bottom that can be stacked. A tray with a narrow, easily guardable opening for the bees is placed under the bottom box of the hive. A lid seals the top. The hive boxes are organized so the bees produce and care for the larval bees in the bottom "brood boxes." The top boxes of a bee hive are called supers. The queen is excluded from entering the supers by an excluder (a wire mesh plate with holes just large enough for workers to pass but too small for the larger queen to squeeze through). Since larvae are reared in the very cells where the queen lays her eggs, the excluder ensures that the brood will be confined to the brood boxes. The excluder allows the workers to store honey in the supers. This makes it possible to remove supers full of honey without disrupting the brood.

How Is Honey Collected?

Hive boxes have removable frames to make it easy to remove the comb. The frames are fitted with beeswax templates so that the comb will be close-packed. Bees will use the hexagons stamped on the template as a guide to placing the cells. The template allows the tightest packing of cells in the hive. When it is time to collect honey, the beekeepers will remove the supers. The frames are removed one by one. Beekeepers extract the honey by cutting the caps off the comb and placing the frame into a spinning extractor. The centrifugal force flings the honey out of the comb and onto the sides of the extractor. The honey flows down the side of the extractor and is collected in the bottom.

Where Was Honey First Collected?

Honey bees originated in Africa. Ancient pictures show humans harvesting honey from bee nests in hive trees. A traditional method of honey harvesting was to build a fire to smoke out the bees and collect the honey from the empty nest.

Where Were Bees First Domesticated?

Honey bees were first domesticated in Egypt over 3000 years ago. The bees were kept in special hive pots made of clay. From Egypt, domestication of honey bees spread to Europe and Asia. Honey was the primary sweetener of Europe, Asia and Africa until the opening of trade between Europe and the Americas. Sugarcane is native to the Americas, and was unknown to Europeans until the late fifteenth century. In much of the world, sugar has replaced honey as the primary dietary sweetener.

How Did the Honey Bee Come to America?

The honey bee is not native to the Americas. European settlers introduced the honey bee to Eastern North America. The honey bee displaced many of the native bee pollinators of North American plants. The honey bee spread from east to west across North America and coincided with the movement of European settlers. Among Native Americans, the honey bee was known as "white man's fly."

How Is Honey Bee Society Structured?

Honey bee colonies contain three castes—workers, drones, and a queen. The workers are sterile females that do all the work of maintaining the colony. A single honey bee queen (female reproductive) is the only female that mates. The queen bee lays all the eggs. All the bees in the hive are her offspring. The male bees (drones) do no work in the hive and do not feed themselves. The worker bees must maintain the males. When winter comes, the workers will eject the high maintenance drones from the hive and they starve.

How Are Queen Bees Produced?

In hives with a productive queen who lays plenty of eggs, the worker bees will produce only workers from the female eggs. The larvae are fed a diet of bee bread (pollen plus nectar) that allows them to grow into workers, but not queens. If the queen is absent from a colony or the fertility of the queen declines, the worker bees will produce new queens. To produce a queen, the workers first make a larger cell from three standard cells. The larvae are fed a special diet of "royal jelly" that is more nutritious than the bee bread. The greater nutrition allows these female larvae to grow into queens with fully functional reproductive systems instead of sterile workers. When a queen is replaced, multiple queens are typically produced, but only one will survive. If multiple queens are present in a hive, the queens will kill each other by fighting and stinging. There is only one queen per hive.

What Is Swarming?

When the queen ages, she may leave the nest with a swarm of workers. The swarm will fly to a new location, often a tree branch. Workers land next to the queen and form a protective ball with the queen at the center. Some workers (scout bees) will search for a new nest site. If a suitable site is found, the workers will return to the swarm and communicate its location by a waggle dance. The swarm will move to the new site and begin a new colony. When the swarm is outside the colony, they have no nest to defend and are less aggressive and less likely to sting. Once they move into the new nest, they will defend it aggressively.

What Happens to the Old Hive?

In a hive that has lost its queen and her swarm, the workers will produce new queens from some of the eggs. The new queens will hatch and fight to the death until only one queen remains. That queen will take a mating flight, then return to the hive and continue the colony.

What Happens to Swarms?

Beekeepers can collect honey bee swarms and place them in a hive. There are special traps for honey bees that resemble honey trees. The traps are ideal locations for a honey bee nest. A beekeeper can place a trap near the swarm and almost always the swarm will move in within a day. At night the bees can be shut in the trap and transported to a standard hive where the beekeeper can care for them.

How Do Honey Bees Mate?

The drone honey bees fly in mating swarms to attract and mate with females. Unmated queens will fly into the swarm of drones and mate with the fastest flying male. The honey bees mate in the air. The male will couple with the female, and then do a back flip that breaks off his reproductive organs. The male reproductive organs have muscles that continue to pump the sperm into the female after the male is gone. The male falls to the ground and dies.

How Often Do Queen Bees Mate?

The female will mate with up to a dozen males. The multiple matings all occur during a single nuptial flight by the queen. The sperm are stored in the reproductive system of the queen. She will need millions of sperm to produce millions of female workers and a few new queens.

How Do Queens Produce Workers and Drones?

Each worker egg is fertilized with a sperm. Drone eggs are unfertilized. The queen controls the fertilization process so that the vast majority of bees in the hive are female workers from fertilized eggs. Very few unfertilized eggs are laid.

How Do Bees Develop within the Hive?

Each colony has one queen that lays all the eggs. The queen is fed and groomed by workers. A queen can lay up to 1,500 eggs/day. The worker bees prepare brood cells from beeswax. The queen lays one egg in each cell. The egg will hatch into a bee larva. The workers feed and care for the larva until it pupates. The workers then seal the pupa in its cell. When it emerges as an adult, it chews through the wax to leave the cell.

How Is the Work of the Hive Organized?

Bees have an age-based division of labor. Young workers do simple tasks within the hive and progress to more complex tasks as they age.

Bees less than one week old are "cleaner bees." Cleaner bees eat dead larvae and clean wax cells.

Bees two to two and a half weeks old become "nurse bees" that feed and groom larvae.

Bees three to three and a half weeks old become "builder bees" that use wax glands to build comb in nest. A few at this age become "undertaker bees" that remove dead bees from hive.

Among the oldest bees in the hive are "guard bees" that challenge intruders and alert defender bees to disturbance.

Only the oldest bees leave the hive. Bees four to six weeks old may become "forager bees." Nectar, pollen, water, and propolis (bee glue), the tree resin used to seal the hive are all collected by forager bees.

Some of the older bees are "defender bees" that are stimulated by alarm pheromone emitted by guard bees to fly from the colony to sting intruders.

The most dangerous tasks such as defense and foraging are performed by the oldest bees that have the shortest remaining life span. The youngest bees, with the most life span remaining, perform the safest tasks within the protection of the hive.

How Do Honey Bees Communicate?

Honey bees have a true symbolic language that is communicated through body movements. On a vertical surface in a special area of the hive, returning foragers will communicate to other foragers in the hive. The round and waggle dances communicate information on location and distance of resources from the hive.

A **round dance** is a circular movement by a returning forager indicating that resources are within 30 meters of the hive. The round dance does not communicate direction.

A **waggle dance** is a figure eight dance. The returning forager moves in a straight line on the vertical surface. The angle of the straight line from straight up vertical indicates the horizontal angle relative to the sun. The length of the line indicates the distance to the resource. After completing the straight run the bee alternatively loops to the left and the right on its return to the start of the straight run. The intensity of the waggle dance is related to the quality of the resource.

How Do Bees Sting?

If a larger intruder attacks a bee hive, defender bees will attack the intruder. In addition to stinging, the intruder, the bees will release a chemical that acts as an alarm pheromone. The odor attracts other bees to the intruder and directs the attack. The alarm pheromone odor used by bees and some wasps is similar to the solvents used in nail polish remover. Removing nail polish outside may alarm nearby bees and wasps encouraging them to sting.

The stinger of the worker bee is a modified ovipositor. The stingers of worker bees contain **barbs** that hook in the skin of an intruder after the worker flies away. The detachment of the stinger is analogous to the detachment of drone reproductive organs during mating. A muscular venom sac is attached to the bee stinger. The honey bee venom sac contracts and pumps venom into the intruder long after the worker detaches and dies. The venom sac should be removed by scraping not squeezing. Grabbing or squeezing the venom sac may force the entire contents into the victim. Beekeepers use the edge of their hive tool to scrape off stings. Any object with a thin edge or a fingernail can be used as a scraper. The scraper should be pushed so the stinger backs out the way it was inserted.

The sting of the queen bee is straight and needle-like. Inside the abdomen is a venom sack that connects to the stinger via a duct. Queen bees can sting other queens without the stinger detaching. Worker bees do not typically lose their stingers if they are used on other insects. Stingers only detach when they are used on large animals with skin.

How Do Bee Stings Cause Allergies?

Allergies are a reaction of the immune system to foreign proteins. The venoms of bees and wasps contain proteins that can trigger the allergic reaction. Some people have severe allergies to bee venom and can go into anaphylactic shock if stung. Allergic people may choose to carry an "EpiPen," an injection of epinephrine that will counter the anaphylaxis.

What Are "Killer Bees?"

Killer bees are a subspecies of honey bee *(Apis mellifera)* originally from Africa. Commercial bees are a subspecies of *Apis mellifera* that come from docile, European colonies that have been domesticated for centuries. The African subspecies has the same venom, same size, and appearance of the European bees. The African and European bees will inter-mate. It is not possible to distinguish European bees from Africanized bees by appearance alone.

The African bees differ in several important behaviors. Colonies of Africanized bees have more guards, have more defenders, are more willing to attack and sting, remain agitated longer, and chase intruders farther.

Encounters with African bees commonly result in larger numbers of stings. People with limited mobility who are unable to run from the area may be stung to death (thus, the name "killer bees.")

How Did Killer Bees Reach the United States?

European bees are not well adapted to hot tropical climates. A Brazilian bee keeper imported bees from Africa as part of a breeding program to produce hardier bees. The imported bees were overly aggressive and had numerous undesirable traits. Unfortunately, the bees escaped captivity. Because they are aggressive, they displace the domesticated bees and can take over hives. The Africanized bees were better adapted to South and Central America and spread throughout South America. Populations progressively moved north through Central America until they reached the southern United States. Africanized bees are a problem for bee keepers, who must monitor their colonies and destroy the over-aggressive ones.

Killer Bees in Indiana?

Killer bees cannot over-winter in Indiana because they store less food than the European bees. Typically, they do not store enough food to survive our winter. However, bees are commonly transported and queens are bred in the southern United States, so it is possible that killer bee colonies could be in Indiana in the summer.

What Products Do We Get from Bees?

Many bee products are marketable as foods and other uses. Honey is still an important sweetener in much of the world. Bee pollen can be purchased in health food stores as a dietary supplement. Beeswax is used in making candles and is a preferred wax for wax museum figures. Beeswax candles are noted for their clean burning properties.

Do Bees Have Enemies?

Honey bees have many enemies including mites (arachnid relatives of spiders) and other insects. Since the 1990s, North American honey bees have been infested with Varroa mites and tracheal mites. These mites can kill bee colonies if not treated, forcing beekeepers to use selective miticides or other control measures to reduce mite populations. The extra work has reduced the numbers of beekeepers in the United States. Additionally, these mites have eliminated most of the feral (wild) honey bee colonies in the United States. This has created a greater reliance on bee keepers to provide bees for pollination. The most important insect pest of bees is the small hive beetle.

What Are Other Threats to Bees?

Urban sprawl is reducing the area where bees are kept. Some people object to living near honey bees and there may be issues with allergies. Urban sprawl may reduce the plant resources available for foraging. Bees are especially susceptible to some pesticides. It is illegal to use many pesticides on crops that are bee pollinated when the crops are flowering. This is necessary to protect the bees.

What Is Colony Collapse Disorder?

Colony collapse disorder (CCD) is a syndrome characterized by rapid dwindling of the hive without dead bees observed nearby.   CCD appears to be localized and has not been observed in Indiana. During the winter of 2006-2007, many honey bee colonies suffered unusually high mortality. Large numbers of colonies were lost. Researchers at Purdue and their collaborators are investigating factors that negatively impact bee health. This includes surveys of pathogens in bees, inoculating caged bees with pathogens and monitoring pesticides in hives.

Colony collapse created a shortage of honey bees. Growers paid more for pollination services and the reduced pollination caused lower yields. This affected consumers by increasing produce prices.

Ants

Strength in Numbers

Ants are familiar to almost everyone. This is because ants are unavoidable. Ants can live everywhere that man can live except the polar regions of earth. Ants can occasionally become pests when they enter our homes and try to take our food for their own.

There are about 11,000 species of ants. Less than 2 percent of all insect species are ants. However, ants are greater than 33 percent of the insect biomass. The biomass of ants is four times greater than biomass of land vertebrates. Measured by numbers of individuals, ants are the most numerous land animal on the planet. Almost everyone is familiar with ants because they are present in such large numbers.

Ant History

Ants are in the order Hymenoptera and are grouped in a single family the Formicidae. The Formicidae is a branch of the Hymeoptera that is closely related to wasps such as hornets. The evolutionary history of the Hymenoptera starts between 250 and 200 million years ago (mya). Between 250 and 100 mya, the Hymenoptera diversified and produced groups such as the sawflies and the parasitoids evolved. The wasps that are the ancestors of ants are descended from these groups. These ancestral groups of the ants required millions of years to evolve. Ant fossils date to about 100 mya.

Characteristics

All ants belong to a single family the Formicidae. The Formicidae are named after formic acid, a chemical produced by many species of ants. Some anthills reek of formic acid. Formic acid is a preservative with antibacterial and anti-mite agent activity.

Wings

Most of the ants that people encounter are wingless. However, ant reproductives that leave the colony to mate and start new colonies have wings that are similar to wasps. Ant wings are typically transparent membranes. The forewing is larger than the hindwing.

Another characteristic of bees and wasps is a constriction in the abdomen. The constriction allows the abdomen substantial freedom of movement. For instance, wasps can bend their abdomen under their body (yoga-like) so that the tip is extended in front of the head. This would not be possible without the constriction. Other types of insects such as flies and moths that mimic wasps do not have this constriction, nor do the earliest Hymenoptera groups such as sawflies. Ants can be distinguished from bees and wasps because of a double constriction in the abdomen instead of the single constriction found in other wasps and bees.

Ant Society and Castes

All ants are social. No ants are solitary. Ants have nests. (Army ants are an exception.) The nest is a gathering place for the colony and a site of food storage and care of the young. Ants have the highest form of insect society that includes overlapping generations and shared rearing of offspring.

Like all Hymenoptera, ants have complete metamorphosis. The eggs, larvae, and pupae of ants are under the care and protection of adult ants within the colony. There are male and female ants. Like honey bees, most of the ants within a colony are female ants that do the majority of work. Unlike honey bees, ant colonies may have more than one queen.

Ants have "castes" or different forms that have different roles in the ant society. (Castes are different forms of a single species of social insect.) All ant species have at least three castes: reproductive males, reproductive females, and workers. Male and female ant reproductives look different from the workers. Some ant species have more than one type of worker ant.

Workers

In ant colonies the most numerous individuals are the workers. Workers never have wings. All the workers in an ant colony are sterile females. The worker ants regulate the amount and type of food they give the larvae. Standard nutrition will produce a worker ant. In some species queen production requires a special, nutrient enriched diet. The worker ants produce primarily other workers and very few reproductive females (queens). Worker ants do all the upkeep of the nest, forage for food, defend the nest, and care for the brood. Ants distribute food by regurgitating nutrients to other workers, the queen, and the brood larvae.

Age-Specific Tasks

Most ant species have a division of labor within the worker caste that changes with age of the worker. The youngest workers are most valuable because they have the longest life remaining. The youngest workers do tasks within the safety of the nest. Older workers perform more complex and dangerous tasks such as foraging and guarding that require leaving the nest. Studies show that the brains of adult workers continue to grow and develop with age. With brain development comes the ability to complete complex tasks. Older workers are capable of more complex tasks because of their brain development.

Majors and Minors

Some ant species have workers with discrete differences in physical appearance. Most commonly, the workers differ in size, one worker form being noticeably larger than the other. The larger form is called a "major" and the smaller form a "minor." The majors are typically adapted to specialized tasks, whereas the minors perform more general tasks.

Most species of ants do not have majors and minors. However, some common ants, such as carpenter ants have them. Where majors do exist, they are most often tasked with colony defense. Majors typically have larger heads and mandibles that make them more suitable for defense and these are sometimes called "soldiers."

In some ant species, the majors are adapted to tasks other than defense such as food preparation. One *Solenopsis* species of ant utilizes large seeds as its primary source of food. Many of the seeds are too large for the minor workers to grind. Seed grinding is a task for majors who have larger mandibles on a larger head. The majors remain in the colony. Their sole task is to use their oversized mandibles to grind the seeds that the minors bring them. The *Solenopsis* minors do the general work of the colony including foraging for food, bringing the seeds to the majors and care of the colony.

Males

Like many other Hymenoptera, male ants develop from unfertilized eggs and have only half the number of chromosomes as the females. All male ants are reproductives. The male ants have little role in the colony other than mating. Female workers that do all the work greatly outnumber males. The numbers of males are determined by the queen.

Dispersal forms of male ants have wings. Dispersal often is by large swarms that people sometimes mistake for termite swarms. Most ant species mate in the air similar to honey bees. Male ants are often smaller than females. Small size is advantageous for mating in the air because a smaller male is less likely to cause the female to crash. Like honey bees, most ant males mate only once and die after mating. New colonies are started by the mated queen.

Queens

The reproductive female or "queen" ant is produced from a fertilized egg. Control of whether the female egg becomes a worker or a queen varies among ant species. The development of the queen ant may depend on special factors in the egg, special nutrition by the worker ants, or both, depending on the species. The dispersal forms of female ants have wings. Once the queen settles on a nesting site, the wings break off. Ant wings are ill suited to life in underground nests.

New Colonies

Mated female ants of some species can start a new colony without workers. The female constructs a nest, forages for food, lays eggs, and cares for the young. This process is difficult and most new colonies are not successful. If adults are produced, they become workers and take over the tasks of maintaining the colony and caring for the queen.

Other methods of starting new colonies are budding as occurs with Pharaoh ants and Argentine ants. These ants with very large colonies can have multiple queens. In budding, a remote section of the nest with its own queen and workers becomes separated from the main nest. The "bud" becomes a new independent colony.

What Do Ants Do?

The success of ants is marked by the diversity of species. There are species of ants that are predators, army ants, fungus growers, harvesters, and weavers to name a few. Ants are everywhere in the terrestrial environment except Antarctica.

Red Imported Fire Ant

The red important fire ant is an invasive species in the southern United States. The fire ant is known for its sting and defensive behavior. It will swarm over farm equipment in fields and has been known to sting to the death tethered livestock. Efforts are ongoing to control fire ants and limit their spread.

Carpenter Ants

Carpenter ants are large black ants that commonly enter homes in Indiana. Carpenter ants build nests in wood. Most commonly, their nests are in trees outdoors. However, they occasionally build nests in our homes. Carpenter ants prefer wood that is wet or water damaged. Unlike termites, carpenter ants do not digest or feed on the wood. They build tunnels in the wood and deposit the "sawdust" outside.

Ranchers

Some ants are aphid ranchers. The aphids feed on plant phloem that is high in sugar and low in other nutrients. The aphids excrete copious amounts of plant sugars that can be food for other animals. Mutually beneficial interactions have evolved between some species of aphids and some species of ants. The ants will collect the sugar droplets excreted by the aphids (honeydew) as a source of food. The ants will protect the aphids from predators. Some ants will even transport aphids to new and better host plants and take them back to their nest at night for protection.

Farmers

Many leaves of plants are inedible because they contain toxic chemicals. However, the leaves may support growth of fungus. There are species of ants that use fungus as their primary source of food much the same way that we can eat mushrooms (another type of fungus). These ants collect leaves and place them in dark damp underground chambers ideal for growing fungi. The fungus gets plenty of nutrients from the leaves the ants provide and the ants harvest the fungus for food. Ants were farming millions of years before the first human farmer.

Army Ants

Army ants are noted for their high foraging efficiency. They devour everything in their path. Army ants are so efficient that they quickly deplete the food resources in their foraging range. Army ants must be continually on the move. They move so often they do not spend energy on making nests. The workers carry eggs, larvae, and pupae on a continuous march. A well-defined soldier caste protects the colony while on the move.

In some areas of the world, natives have been reported to punish criminals by staking their body in the path of an army and colony. The army ants cause an extremely painful death by millions of tiny bites.

Mugger Ants

Mugger ants eat prey but do not forage. Instead, several mugger ants will lay about nests of other species. Returning foragers are attacked by the mugger ants, which steal the prey.

Thief Ants

Thief ants make extensive underground tunnels. When they tunnel into the nest of another species, they will steal the food and brood, which they use for food.

Guest Ants

Have you ever had a house guest who outstayed their welcome and refused to leave? Some ant species have the same problem. Guest ants are species of ants that live in nests of other species of ants. Guest ants live off the hard work of their hosts. A bit of trickery is involved. The guest ants are able to acquire the nest odor of the host. The guest ant tricks the host into thinking that the guest is actually one of its sister ants. The guest ants and their offspring are fed and cared for by their hosts. The guests do not forage or otherwise contribute to the work of the colony.

Parasitic Ants

Some ant species are parasitic on other ants. In some interactions, the parasitic ants are much smaller than the host ants. The parasite queen rides the back of the host queen and delivers her eggs to host workers attending the host queen. This way the parasite tricks the host species into rearing her eggs.

Propaganda Substances

Ants recognize their own nest mates by their odor. Nest mates all have the same odor because they share the same food (you are what you eat) and the same environment. Invaders have a different odor. Ants defend their nest by attacking the ants that do not have the correct nest odor. This defense can be defeated with propaganda substances (propaganda = misinformation for deception or control).

Harpagoxenus is an ant that attacks nests of other species. Harpagoxenus coats the ants defending their colony with chemicals called "propaganda substances." The propaganda substances change the odor of the defenders. The coated defenders are attacked by their own nest mates who mistake them for invaders (they do not smell like nest mates). This creates confusion within the colony. Defenders are occupied attacking other defenders and create havoc within the colony. This leaves gaps in the defense and allows the Harpagoxenus to defeat the defenders. The invading ants take over the resources of the ant colonies they invade.

Ants and "Slavery"

Some ant species will take brood from other ant species and bring them to their own nest to serve as workers. This phenomenon is described as "slavery." One species of slaver ants are the Amazon ants of the genus Polyergus. Amazon ants will find and attack colonies of Formica species of ants. When the Amazon ants arrive at the Formica nest, the Formica workers will wall the entrance and defend the nest. The Amazon ants have large mandibles that they use to break through the wall. Once inside, the Amazon ants use large sharp mandibles to pierce the brains of the defenders and kill them.

The Amazon ants will collect brood (pupae and larvae) from the ant colony and bring them back to their own colony. When the slave ants become adults, they will be workers in the colony of the slaver ants.

How Does Slave-Making Happen?

In order for slavery to work, the slaver ants must tolerate the foreign ant species in their own nest. The foreign ants must perform the work of the ant colony and not attack slavers. Both slavers and slaves must tolerate new brood. New workers must tolerate other slaves and slavers. This is only possible because of the way ants recognize nest mates.

How Do Ants Recognize Nest Mates?

Ants recognize nest mates because of their odor. Ants that are in the nest and are reared in the nest acquire the "colony odor." Ants not in nest lack the colony odor.

This can be demonstrated by a simple experiment. Ants can be removed from the nest and reared outside the nest. However, if reintroduced into the nest, the ant will be recognized as "foreign." The other ants in the nest will attack them.

Nest mate recognition is "learned" by adult ants. Ants have a "learning period" that occurs during the first 14 days of adult life. Slave ants are brought into a nest as brood larvae and pupae. Thus when they emerge as adults in a foreign nest, they learn the odor of the new nest and recognize all the occupants as nest mates. The slaves do the same work in their new home that they would have done in their old home. The slaves derive no benefit from this process. The slaver ants benefit by obtaining additional workers that they don't have to raise from eggs.

Ants naturally tolerate brood in their nest so the slave ant brood is not attacked. By the time the slave ants emerge as adults, they will have acquired the colony odor and be treated as a nest mate by the other ants.

Slavery works because:

- Defense response is based on colony odor that is learned as an adult.
- Care of young and work within the nest are based on proximate cues that are similar for slave and slaver ant species.
- Slave ants will respond the same way to cues, whether they are in their own nest or the nest of another species.
- Slaves are only brought into the slaver nest as pupae or larvae never adults.
- Slaver ants and slave ants are both predisposed to nurture larvae and pupae, not attack them even if they do not have colony odor.
- Larvae and pupae of slaves that complete development to adults within the slaver nest acquire the nest odor of the slavers and therefore do not attack and are not attacked by other adults (slave and slaver) within the colony.

Social Insects and Complex Structures

Stigmergy

How do insects "know" how to build a nest and perform other complex tasks in a social environment? The underlying principle is "**stigmergy**, a social phenomenon in which agents interact by affecting their environment rather than communicating directly one to another."

In an insect society individuals work as if alone, but their collective activities appear coordinated. In insect societies a hierarchical command structure does not exist. A queen does not "order workers." Unlike the science fiction stories, ants do not use "telepathy." Instead, workers are born with simple behaviors.

Each individual in a nest is acting on its own. A simple behavior is triggered by an environmental cue. Each individual inherits a stereotypical behavioral response. Each ant responds to an environmental cue in the same way that any other individual will respond. The changes one ant makes to the nest or the landscape provides cues for the next ant that arrives.

Communication By Altering the Environment

Stigmergy relies on changes to the environment. There are three basic ways to change the environment: remove, add, or alter the material. Everything that an ant does from nest building to foraging and brood care involves adding, removing or altering material in the environment. For example, making a burial pile requires removing single dead carcasses and adding each carcass to a growing pile of dead carcasses.

Stigmergic Systems

Foraging by ants is the model of a stigmergic system. Stigmergic systems involve communications among individuals by altering the environment rather than direct communication by symbolic language. Stigmergy has application to computer programming, especially in the development of web browsers that identify which sites are most frequently visited. The main features of a stigmergic system are:

- There are no instructions from a boss.
- Each individual gathers information.
- Each individual acts on information

Because the information comes from shared environment and each individual processes the information in a similar manner, the process appears coordinated even though it is not. There are no centralized decisions, only a few elementary rules.

Ant Pheromone Trails, an Example of a Stigmergic System

Ants use odor to mark the location of food sources. Ants have a trail pheromone gland on the tip of their abdomen that produces a trail pheromone (scent). An ant forager that finds a source of food will transport some of the food back to the nest. As the forager returns to the nest, it marks the ground with trail pheromone. The forager typically uses landmarks to return to the nest.

Foraging ants on the way to find food do not mark with odor. It is only after food is found that the ant will return to the nest with food and mark an odor trail on the return trip. Foragers leaving the nest will follow the pheromone trails created by other individuals. Once they reach the food, the foragers will add more pheromone to the trail on their return to the nest. If there is a substantial amount of food, then each ant using the trail will arrive at the food and reinforce the trail on its return journey. This process reinforces the trail and recruits many ants to the food.

The ant pheromone trail lasts for only a short time, and then dissipates. Trails have to be constantly reinforced to remain active. Once the food is gone, then the foraging ants that have followed the old trail will not return directly to the nest but continue foraging until they find additional food. Those foragers will start a new trail back to the nest from the site of the new food source. The pheromone trail to the exhausted food resource will no longer be reinforced. The trail will dissipate and go away completely.

This system causes trails to be created to current food resources and ensures that the trails will go away when the food is exhausted. There is no overall control or organization of foraging or laying pheromone trails. Each foraging ant acts independently. Trail pheromone turns the landscape into a virtual database that carries pointers to food sources.

Why Are Anthills Round?

How do ants know to build a perfectly round hill? The simple answer is that they don't know. Because many anthills are perfectly round, at first glance one might assume that it is round by design. However, the round shape is a product of a large group of ant individuals, each behaving according to simple rules. The round anthill is the outcome of following the simple rules. None of the individual ants "knows" it is making a round anthill. There is no need for an architect or a construction engineer to direct the work of the ants.

If an ant worker is in an area of the nest that is being expanded, the ant will remove soil particles and carry them outside the nest. Each step away from the nest entrance makes the ant increasingly likely to deposit the soil particles. The anthill is produced by the independent actions of thousands of ant-trips. Because the direction the ants are facing when they leave the nest entrance is random, thousands of ants will distribute the soil relatively equally through all 360 degrees of the compass, a perfect circle. So ants don't know they are making a hill in a perfect circle. The perfect circle is the outcome of thousands of ants randomly acting by following a simple rule.

Burial Piles

Simple rules are involved in nest cleaning. If an ant detects an individual dead carcass and it is not carrying anything, it will pick it up. The ant will only drop it when it detects another dead carcass. This causes all the dead carcasses to be piled together in a trash area of the nest.

Social Insect Cooperative Tasks

Insects must complete long sequences of behaviors to produce a nest or complete other tasks. For solitary insects, the long behavior sequence often must be completed from start to finish without stopping. For solitary insects, if the sequence is not taken to completion, the solitary insect must start the process from the beginning. For example, a digger wasp will first dig a tunnel, and then fly off to find a prey item, bring it back to the nest, lay an egg, and close the tunnel. If the sequence is interrupted at any point (for example, the wasp cannot find the tunnel) the entire sequence must start again.

Starting over could be counterproductive in a social environment. For social insects, tasks are broken down into simple steps. Like an assembly line, social insects complete the next step of complex tasks initiated by others. There is no need to start over if a sequence is only partially completed. Any individual can step into the sequence at any point and complete the work. Breaking the task into smaller increments allows many individuals to contribute to the same task in a cooperative manner. These principles may also apply to human social interactions.

Stigmergic System Applications

Studies of the organization of insect societies provide ideas for human organization. For instance, Internet search engines use the same principle as ant trail pheromone. Web sites that are most often visited get highest ratings within the system. Users navigating to a web site lay down a "marker" (similar to trail pheromone) that is utilized by the search engine. The more hits, the higher the rating (more food the stronger the trail). There are interesting parallels gathered from insect societies that are useful to computer science and social science.

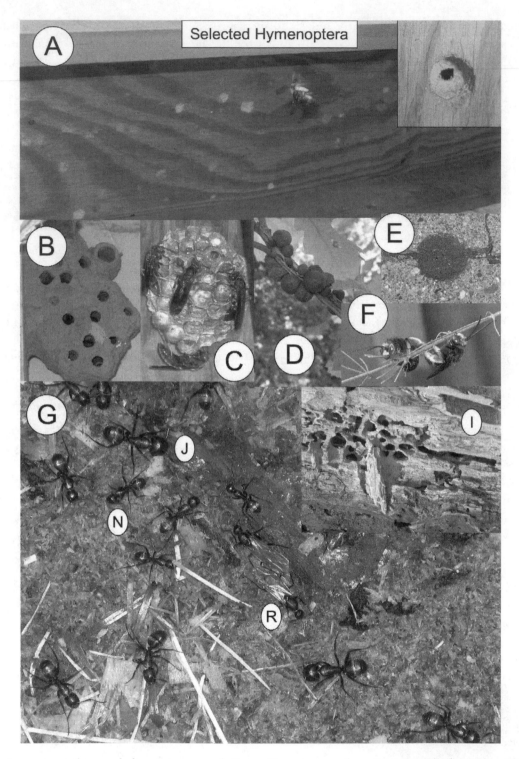

Selected Hymenoptera

A. A carpenter bee and damage to wood. Inset: Entrance to the nest.   B. Mud Dauber Wasp nest.   C. Paper Wasp nest   D. Oak galls made by cynipid gall wasps. The galls can be ground to make a long lasting printing ink.   E. Ant hill. The hill is circular because it is made by the actions of thousands of ant trips each dropping a load of dirt in after leaving the nest in a random direction.   F. Solitary bees   G. Carpenter Ants. J: Majors. N: Minors. R: Alate Reproductives (note the wings). I (inset): Carpenter ant galleries.

A. Ants tending aphids. Note winged aphids (alates) ready for the fall migration.   B. Red aphids feeding on a cup plant.   C. Maple mealy bug. The first instar larvae settle into a feeding site and secrete a waxy material that protects them from predators.   D. Tulip Tree Scale. These sessile insects secrete a hard material that protects them from predators.   E. Wheel bugs are predators, feeding on a variety of insects. They are named after the shape of the thorax that looks like cogs on a wheel.   F. A stink bug feasts on a monarch caterpillar. Many stink bugs are predators. Some are phytophagous.   G. A spittle bug is a sessile feeder that blows air into the plant juices it secretes creating the "spittle". Inset: The bug is protected from predators by the spittle.   H. Soybean aphids feed on a leaf. Note the winged adults. In 2009, very large clouds of soybean aphids were noted in Tippecanoe County, Indiana.   I. The cast skin of a cicada larva. Note that the front legs are modified for digging. The larvac live in the soil and suck plant juices from tree roots.

True Bugs And Their Relatives

There are several orders of related insects that are grouped as "Paraneoptera." These groups include the Hemiptera and related insects such as thrips and lice.

Hemiptera

Hemiptera including the "true bugs" and their close relatives appear in the fossil record over 300 million years ago (mya). The Hemiptera were present when giant insects roamed the earth prior to the appearance of beetles and well before the dinosaurs evolved. Hemiptera have incomplete metamorphosis; there is no pupa stage. The Hemiptera vary in size from tiny aphids (about 1 mm) to large insects over 10 cm long.

Both larvae and adults have sucking mouthparts. The sucking mouthparts are capable of piercing plants and sucking the plant juices. This method of feeding allows these insects to avoid plant defenses against chewing insects. Because they pierce the plants and inject saliva, many insects in this group are important carriers of plant viruses (in much the same way that mosquitoes transmit animal viruses).

The sucking mouthparts can be used by predators. Predatory bugs stab their prey with their syringe-like mouthparts and inject digestive enzymes. These enzymes can paralyze the prey and digest its tissues. The liquefied, digested tissues are pumped into the gut of the bug.

True Bugs

The Hemiptera contains a number of groups. The largest group of Hemiptera are true bugs. True bugs have forewings that are membranous on the tips and hardened on the half attached to the thorax (part membranous, part hardened). (Beetles also have hardened forewings. However, in beetles the entire forewings are hardened and they meet in a straight line down the middle.) True bugs have only half the forewing hardened and the wings overlap when folded. Most of the true bugs feed on plants but some are predaceous. Some of the predaceous bugs such as bed bugs feed on human blood.

Box Elder Bug
Notable insects in this group include the box elder bug, wheel bug, minute pirate bug, and the stink bugs. The box elder bug is a red and black bug that feeds on box elder. Box elder bugs are harmless, but sometimes encountered indoors. They over-winter as adults. In seeking shelter they sometimes find their way into homes.

Wheel Bug
The wheel bug is a large predatory bug that gets its name from a cog-like structure on its thorax that resembles half of a wheel. They are common in Indiana. If handled they pierce the skin with their mouthparts. This causes a sharp pain but is lasts less long than a bee sting. If left alone, wheel bugs are harmless. Wheel bugs provide some benefit by eating pest insects.

Minute Pirate Bugs
Minute pirate bugs are predators of aphids in cornfields. They benefit us by reducing aphid populations. These bugs are voracious predators and will bite people on occasion. When corn is harvested, they sometimes fly to surrounding areas where they find and bite people. They do not feed on people or cause harm, but their bites are irritating.

Stink Bugs

Stink bugs are typically over 1 cm in length and prey on other insects. Stink bugs have glands that release defensive chemicals when disturbed. Handling a stink bug can make your hand stink for several hours. Stink bugs can feed on caterpillars and other insects that have defensive spines and hairs. The defense works to prevent chewing insects from reaching the prey. However, the sharp, heavily sclerotized mouthparts of stink bugs can maneuver past the defensive hairs and spines and pierce the prey at a safe distance from the rest of its body.

Bed Bugs

Bed bugs infest bedding, bite people, and can cause skin irritation. There is currently a resurgence of bed bug infestations in the United States. Bed bugs are increasingly reported from cruise ships and hotels, even in five-star hotels. Bed bugs are not related to cleanliness. Bed bug infestations are eliminated by insecticide treatments and removing contaminated bedding.

Staying in a bed bug infested hotel room can result in bringing home an infestation as a souvenir. It is wise to check for bed bugs. This involves pulling down covers to check for moving insects or small reddish or black spots. The spots are caused by bed bug excretions. If you find bed bugs, ask for another room or try another lodging. If bed bugs are feeding on you, pick them off. Drop them in rubbing alcohol or flush them down the toilet. Bed bugs do not strongly attach (like ticks) and are easily removed. If bed bugs are in your room, check suitcases and clothing. Upon your return home, you may want to unpack your suitcase outside, wash clothing, and vacuum the luggage. Placing mothballs in your luggage is effective bed bug control.

Bed bugs at home can be difficult to eliminate. It is necessary to spray with appropriate insecticide. Bed bugs hide in hard to reach locations during the day and commonly escape pesticide treatments that are not thorough enough. Many people prefer to call an exterminator who is trained to do the job effectively and safely.

Aquatic Bugs

Aquatic bugs include water striders, water boatmen, and giant water bugs.

Water Boatmen

Water boatmen have legs built like oars for rowing in the water. They have special hairs that push against the water on the fore stroke and fold down on the backstroke. Water boatmen swim underwater near the bottom. They feed on algae and aquatic plants by injecting them with saliva, then sucking up the digested plant cells.

Water Striders

Water striders walk on water. Water striders have special hairs on the ends of their feet that create a meniscus on the water. The legs of water striders cover a large enough area that the surface tension of the water holds them afloat. The water striders can push against the water to row across the surface.

Water striders are predators of small aquatic animals. They inject their prey with digestive enzymes (external digestion) and suck in the digested tissues of their prey. They can be opportunistic and capture insects that have fallen into the water and are unable to swim or get out of the water.

Giant Water Bugs

Giant water bugs are predators. (These are different from the cockroaches that some people call "water bugs.") Water bugs swim underwater and capture small aquatic animals including insects and small fish. To protect their eggs, the female glues the eggs to the back of the male. Egg predators are deterred because they might be food for the male, rather than making a meal of the eggs.

Not "True Bugs"

The Hemiptera that are not "true bugs" have two completely membranous wings of roughly the same size and shape. All of these insects feed on plants. The sucking mouthparts can be inserted into plants to selectively feed on plant fluids. They can avoid some of the plant defenses against chewing insects.

Aphids

Aphids feed on plant fluids that are rich in sugar, but deficient in a many nutrients. Aphids consume excess plant fluids in order to get enough nutrients. They excrete excess sugar as a sticky substance called "honeydew." The honeydew is an important food for many other insects. Aphids are commonly found on sycamore trees in the summer. Parking your car under a sycamore can result in your windshield becoming a sticky mess from the honeydew secreted by aphids.

Some ants have evolved relationships with aphids. The ants protect the aphids and move them onto host plants. The ants collect the honeydew from the aphids. The honeydew provides ants with a good source of food for their colony.

Large populations of aphids can harm plants by depleting their energy stores. Aphids are also important vectors of plant viruses. Aphids can inject viruses directly into phloem, bypassing the plant defenses.

Scale insects, **whiteflies,** and **mealy bugs** are close relatives of aphids. They also suck on plant fluids. These insects are pests of trees and ornamental houseplants. They damage the plants and detract from their appearance. It is a good idea to inspect nursery plants for insects and remove them before taking the plants home.

Spittlebugs are insects that produce froth around their body as they feed on plants. The froth protects them from predators. Spittlebugs are common in meadows. We more often see the spittle than the spittle bugs. When disturbed, spittlebugs can jump amazingly long distances. A spittlebug holds the record for jumping the longest distance relative to body length (400 times) of any animal.

Leafhoppers are important plant pests. The potato leafhopper can cause damage to plants by feeding on the leaves. These leafhoppers are attracted to lights and hundreds of the tiny green insects can be seen at night on windows in late spring. The potato leafhopper is migratory, using weather fronts to travel long distances.

Unlike the monarch butterfly that powers its own migration, the potato leafhopper takes advantage of weather patterns. The potato leafhopper overwinters in the Gulf States of the southern United States. Leafhoppers have the ability to sense changes in air pressure that are associated with major weather systems. In spring many storms move rapidly from southwest to northeast. Leafhoppers fly up into the storm and hitch a ride north. Because they are hitching a ride, the time of arrival of leafhoppers in an area changes from year to year. In Indiana, we often see leafhoppers in April during the beginning of tornado season.

In the fall, leafhoppers hitch a ride on storm systems moving from north to south to return to the Gulf States. Migration is one way that some insects survive the winter.

Cicadas

Cicadas are the largest and most obvious members of this group. Cicada larvae live underground and feed on the roots of trees. The adult male cicadas make a loud sound to attract females for mating.

There are two major types of cicadas in the United States—dog day cicada and periodic cicada. The dog day cicada emerges every year and can be heard calling from mid to late summer. August in Indiana is called the "dog days of summer," hence the name dog day cicada. Dog day cicadas are the prey of cicada killer wasps as well as many birds.

Periodic Cicadas

Periodic cicadas require many years to complete development. The larvae spend 16 years underground feeding on tree roots and emerge in the seventeenth year as adults. Massive numbers emerge in spring (May–June). The chorusing can reach over 120 decibels (loud enough to cause ear pain).

The mass emergence is a "predator satiation" technique. Predators consume defenseless cicadas until they are full. Only a small fraction of the cicada population is eaten; most of the cicadas escape predation.

The female cicadas lay eggs in the ends of tree branches. The twigs with the eggs will break off, and eventually fall to the ground. Egg lying produces substantial "leaf flagging" (brown wilted leaves) on the trees.

Periodic cicadas are in broods that cover contiguous geographic areas. Broods emerge in different years in different geographic locations. The next brood in Indiana is due in 2021.

The Psocid Group

The Psocids are related to the Hemiptera, but have chewing mouthparts instead of sucking mouthparts. Some of the insects in this group have important interactions with people.

Book Lice

Book lice are all females and reproduce parthenogenically. Book lice require high humidity and will desiccate if the air is dry. Book lice feed on mold and mildew. Book lice can be eliminated from libraries and library collections by proper sanitation. This is one reason why libraries with valuable old books do not allow food. Food could potentially be contaminated and spread booklice. Also, spilled food could promote mold and mildew that support book lice infestations.

Lice

Lice also belong to the Psocid group. There are many species of lice. Most are adapted to a single host species. Humans have two species of lice parasites. These are the head (or body) lice and the pubic (or crab) lice. Human lice are economically and medically important. Before the widespread use of insecticides and modern hygiene, most humans carried lice.

Head or Body Lice
Head lice are the most common lice and are controlled in part by quarantine. School children with lice are suspended from school until the infestation is eliminated. This has become more difficult as lice have become resistant to many treatments. Head lice are transferred by contact

with infested people or their clothing and bedding. Sharing hats or sleepovers are common ways of transferring lice.

Lice have claws on the ends of their legs that they use for grasping hair. The lice walk on the hair, not the skin and cling to the hair. They crawl down the shaft of the hair to the skin to feed. Human lice have sucking mouthparts and feed on human blood.

Head lice eggs are "glued" to hairs and are called "nits." Nits can be removed by careful combing, although it is time consuming. There are some insecticidal shampoo treatments for lice. The treatment is less effective against the eggs than the larvae and adults. The nits must be picked off or multiple treatments are necessary.

Recent genetic evidence has suggested that head lice and body are a single species. Body lice are known to transmit typhus. After World War II, large populations of homeless people in Europe were at risk for typhus epidemics. Several epidemics were averted by the use of DDT to kill the lice.

Pubic Lice

Pubic lice are confined to the pubic region. Contrary to urban legend, they are not viable for long if not in contact with a host. Pubic lice require intimate contact for transmission. They can NOT be transmitted by infested toilet seats.

Grasshoppers, Katydids, And Crickets

The order Orthoptera is ancient and contains many familiar insects including grasshoppers, katydids and crickets. The earliest orthopteran fossils are over 300 million years old. Most of the extant groups of Orthoptera were present during the Carboniferous, long before dinosaurs roamed the earth. These groups survived the massive extinction at the end of the Permian period.

The name "Orthoptera" comes from the Latin "ortho" = straight and "ptera" = wing. Straight wing describes the shape of the Orthoptera wing when it is held at rest. The leading edge of the wing is straight.

The Orthoptera evolved and diversified prior to the evolution of complete metamorphosis. Insects with incomplete metamorphosis have only three stages—an egg, larva, and adult. No pupa stage is present. The Orthoptera all have larvae that resemble miniature adults, minus wings and reproductive organs. The wings develop gradually with each molt and appear as external wing pads. As the size of the larva increases with each molt, the wing pads are progressively larger. The adult wings develop within the wing pads of the last instar (stage) larva.

Key features of the Orthoptera are hind legs modified for jumping, and communication by sound. Protective coloration (crypsis) is common in this group.

Katydids

Katydids are sometimes called long-horned grasshoppers because of the characteristic antennae that are longer than the body. Katydids are active at night and the long antenna can detect potential predators at a safe distance.

Katydids are primarily herbivores, feeding on plant foliage. Many katydids have protective coloration and resemble the leaves of the plants they eat. Intense selection by predators has led to the evolution of katydids that mimic some of the finer features of their host plants. These katydid mimics match the color of their host plant and some may have patterns that resemble plant diseases or insect feeding.

Katydid is named after its song, a series of short bursts that can be described as "KAY-TEE-DID." The song is produced by special structures on the wings. Typically, the males call and the females are silent. Calling can attract enemies. Remaining silent protects the female. Katydids are most active at night, a behavior that avoids bird predators. Katydids typically call at night. Their long antennae allow them to locate mates in the dark or detect potential predators at a safer distance.

Katydids are closely related to crickets and novices sometimes confuse the two. The famous Mormon cricket is really a katydid. Mormon crickets do not fly well and move by hopping or jumping. The early Mormon settlers in Utah experienced a plague of "crickets" that were devastating their crops (thus their name). According to legend, gulls that arrived and ate the Mormon crickets ended the plague. To commemorate this event, a gull statue was erected in Salt Lake City. Entomologists think that the gulls would have had a minimal effect on reducing the Mormon cricket population and that the population was more likely eliminated by diseases that spread among outbreak insect populations.

Crickets

Crickets are closely related to katydids and also chirp with their wings. Katydid wings are held tent-like over their body while cricket wings are flattened over their body. Like katydids, crickets have long antennae and are nocturnal.

The common house cricket is a native of Europe that was introduced to North America in the 1700s. The house cricket was one of the first invasive species. House crickets hide in crevices and invade houses. They are omnivorous and chew on food and clothing. They destroy possessions, eat food, and are noisy.

Crickets are commonly used as food for pets, especially reptiles. Crickets can be purchased commercially, although some pet owners prefer to rear their own crickets. Crickets eat almost anything. However, the quality of the cricket as food for your pet depends on what the cricket is fed. Some businesses have developed "gut-loading" kits for sale to pet owners. These kits contain food that is given to crickets prior to feeding them to pets. Gut-loading is a way of increasing the nutritional value of the crickets as pet food.

Grasshoppers

Grasshoppers typically have shorter antennae than crickets or katydids and are active during the day. Grasshoppers are generalist herbivores that typically "graze" on numerous species of plants. Grasshoppers take many small meals from a large variety of plants. This helps grasshoppers avoid too much toxin from any one plant.

Grasshoppers have several defense mechanisms. Most grasshoppers have protective coloration that makes them difficult to detect when they are not moving. If disturbed, adult grasshoppers will hop or fly away. The wings often have bright colors that distract the predators during flight, and then disappear when the wings are folded as the grasshopper lands. This makes the grasshopper more difficult for predators to track. If handled, most grasshoppers will regurgitate their gut contents. This liquid is deterrent to many predators. Children sometimes refer to grasshopper regurgitation as "tobacco juice."

Grasshopper Flight
The forewings of grasshoppers are leathery and straight, whereas the hindwings are membranous and more expansive. Flying grasshoppers hold their forewings laterally and flap the more expansive

hind wings. The forewing serves as an airfoil to provide glide and lift. The hind wings power the flight.

Plague Locusts

The plague locusts of Australia, North Africa, and Asia are grasshoppers. The plague locust is a species of grasshopper that travels in large swarms. When the swarm descends, they devour all the foliage in the area. When resources are depleted, the locusts take flight to bring misery to a new area. Locust plagues have devastated crops since the dawn of human agriculture and are reported in some of the earliest historical documents. (Some people in the United States will call cicadas "locusts." However, cicadas have few similarities to the Orthoptera and are not related to plague locusts.)

Grasshoppers are edible. Some people compensate for the loss of their crops to locusts by eating the locusts.

Stick And Leaf Insects

The stick and leaf insects are herbivores, feeding primarily on leaves. These insects are masters of crypsis, bearing close resemblance to the plants they eat and live on. Like the Orthoptera, they have chewing mouthparts and incomplete metamorphosis. However, they lack saltatory (jumping) hind legs and do not communicate by sounds.

Stick Insects

Stick mimics include some of the largest insects. The giant stick insect of New Zealand can reach over 30 cm (1 foot) in length. These stick insects have several lines of defense. The initial defense is crypsis. They are difficult to see when they are on their host plant because they resemble sticks. They remain motionless during the day, making them more difficult to detect. They move and feed at night.

If disturbed, giant stick insects open their wings to display warning colors. If a predator attacks and grasps a leg, the leg will break off and the insect will drop to the ground. Some stick insects produce toxins that make them distasteful to predators.

The giant stick insect can catapult its frass away from the feeding site to avoid detection. A large pile of frass on the ground underneath its feeding site could be a dead giveaway. Catapulting the frass prevents predators from using this cue. Eggs of the giant stick insect resemble seeds and drop to the ground.

Stick insects are noted for extreme sexual dimorphism. Females can be substantially larger than males. Females need extra nutrition to make eggs and a larger abdomen for egg production.

Many adult stick insects are wingless, including the most common stick insect in Indiana. In many stick insects with wings, the male will fly but the female does not. Like moths, female stick insects produce a pheromone to attract males. Compared to females, males typically have longer antennae that are more sensitive to the pheromone.

Leaf Insects

Leaf insects resemble leaves, dead leaves, lichens, or other plants in their environment. Leaf insects have evolved radical changes in appearance that blend with their host plants. Leaf insects are subject to intense predation, primarily from birds that use visual cues to find their prey. Those insects that are most difficult to see are most likely to survive and produce offspring. The genes for blending into the surroundings are inherited by their offspring. After many generations and cycles of selection, leaf insects have evolved uncanny resemblances to their host plants. In addition to color and shape, some leaf insects mimic very fine details of leaves including common disease spots.

Stoneflies

Stoneflies are an order of about 2000 species that have aquatic larvae. Stonefly larvae are predatory and active year round. Some species may take more than 1 year to develop to adult. Stoneflies are sensitive to water quality and the amount of oxygen in the water. The disappearance of stonefly larvae from an area indicates that the quality of the water has declined due to pollution or other disturbance.

Winter stoneflies have adults that emerge on sunny days in the middle of winter. Adults mate, lay their eggs in the water, and die. By flying in the winter they are able to avoid predation by birds (gone for the winter) and fish that have ceased feeding.

Earwigs

Earwigs are notable for the prominent forceps-like cerci at the end of the abdomen. The cerci may be used for a variety of purposes including copulation or grasping prey. The name "earwig" is so old that its origin has been forgotten. Three possible origins of "earwig" are that 1) the insects were ground to produce an ear medicine, 2) the forceps-like cerci resemble devices used to pierce ears, or 3) earwigs can crawl in people's ears.

Earwigs rarely crawl in ears, but there are at least two confirmed reports. The idea of earwigs crawling into ears and eating the brain is urban legend. The eardrum typically stops earwigs in the ear, although they may pierce it. Earwigs that inadvertently enter ears usually leave when they get hungry.

The idea of earwigs eating the brain has been exploited for insect fear stories and TV shows. Oscar Cook wrote the story, "Boomerang" about a man who hired an assassin to place an earwig in the ear of his rival. This story was made into an episode of the Rod Serling Show, "Night Gallery." In the story, the assassin accidentally puts the earwig into the ear of the villain behind the plot instead of his rival. After the earwig eats some of his brain, the villain is relieved to find the earwig emerging from his other ear. The show ends with an entomologist delivering the bad news to the villain that the earwig was a female that probably laid eggs inside his head. Great fiction, but entirely false and an urban legend. Earwigs on rare occasions may enter a human ear. However, they do NOT chew their way into the brain. Still if you sleep in areas crawling with insects, you might consider earplugs.

Selected Orthopteroids

A. Earwig. Note the characteristic cerci on the end of the abdomen.   B. Katydid or long-horned grasshopper. They are typically active at night and are cryptically colored to blend in with plant foliage. Note the long antennae   C. Grasshopper. Note short antennae   D. Grasshopper has cryptic coloration that blends into the background.   E. Giant stick insect. Note the expansion of the leg surface to resemble leaflets.   F. Giant stick insect. Note size relative to the dime. Stick insects are some of the largest of all insects.   G. Praying mantis. Note the characteristic triangular head,

(*continued on page 153*)

Chapter 9 • Notable Groups of Insects

Mantids

Mantids are predatory insects. Mantids have raptorial forelegs, an elongated prothorax and are cryptic. The mantid strategy for capturing prey is "stay and slay." Mantids have coloration that blends with the plant parts or environment they inhabit. Many mantids are leaf mimics but mantids may also mimic flowers, other plant parts or even the soil surface. Mantids that mimic flowers take advantage of the flower's attraction to flying insects.

Mantids eat a variety of prey. The prey changes as the mantid grows. Small mantids can be fed small flies such as fruit flies and larger mantids can graduate to a variety of larger insects. Insects that are too small may escape capture by large mantids. Some mantids are hosts to kleptoparasite flies. These flies ride on the backs of mantids. When the mantid grasps a prey, the fly will land on the prey and steal a meal.

Mantid eggs are laid in groups within a protective egg case. Some supply houses will sell mantid egg cases to gardeners for insect control. Unfortunately, mantids are cannibalistic and disperse to low densities. As biological control agents, they are not very effective. They typically do not eat enough prey to significantly reduce the prey population.

Mating is difficult for any predatory insect. The male must be identified by the female as a mate and not mistaken for a prey item. Like stick insects, males are frequently smaller than females and female mantids have pheromones to attract mates.

In some species, the female will eat the male mantid after mating occurs. Because of the low population density, males rarely have an opportunity to mate more than once. The nutrients accumulated by the male mantid can be used to provision eggs. This maximizes the number of offspring that a single male can produce. In other mantids, the males escape intact after mating. However, in captivity, males that cannot escape after mating will be eaten.

Cockroaches

Cockroach fossils date to over 300 million years ago (mya). Cockroaches are survivors of multiple extinction events including the End of Permian extinction 251 mya and the dinosaur extinction 65 mya. Cockroaches are scavengers, feeding on dead plants and detritus. Occasionally, they may

(plate caption *continued*)

extended pro-thorax and raptorial forelegs. The cryptic coloration of the praying mantis protects it from predators and conceals it from potential prey.   H. An American cockroach, darkening an apartment doorstep, is one of only a dozen species of cockroach that is a common household pest.   I. The Madagascar "hissing" cockroaches are kept as pets by some hobbyists. They are not pests because the rate of reproduction is low and they fail to thrive indoors.   J. The wood roach is commonly found under logs or in wood chips in Indiana.   K. A termite worker. Note the beaded antennae and lack of eyes. Termites are the most important pest of human structures and cause large economic damage.   L. Termite traps are used for monitoring and controlling termite populations. The traps are baited with paper and placed with the top level to the ground. If termites are found in a trap, the paper is replaced with a slow acting insecticide that is carried back to nest by termite foragers and spread throughout the colony by sharing food (trophallaxis).

eat some live plant material but that is typically a very minor part of cockroach diet. Because they are scavengers, cockroaches are unlikely to be without food, even after catastrophic events such as asteroid collisions. Cockroaches have a global distribution. They are present on all continents.

Over 4,000 species of cockroaches have been described but fewer than twelve species are considered pests. Most cockroaches live outdoors and seldom contact humans or our possessions. The largest extant cockroach, found in Australia, is over 3 inches long. Fossil cockroaches that are slightly larger have been found in Ohio.

Cockroaches have a flattened body. The head is covered by an extension of the thorax. This body plan allows the cockroach to fit into cracks and crevices. The thorax protects the head. Cockroaches prefer to harbor in cracks and crevices because it provides protection against many predators. Most cockroaches are active at night.

Most cockroach species have wings and can fly as adults, although some species lack wings. Common pest cockroaches in Indiana, such as the German, brown-banded, and American cockroaches, do not fly. Flying Asian cockroaches have recently been introduced into Florida. Fortunately, the Asian cockroaches seldom enter human habitats.

Cockroaches are most closely related to the mantids and share several characters. Both the mantids and cockroaches produce egg cases that contain many eggs. The egg cases are called ootheca. The ootheca of the German cockroach is hard, due to sclerotin in its cuticle. The female of the German cockroach carries her ootheca with her until the eggs hatch. The ootheca partially protrudes from the reproductive tract. About a day before the eggs hatch the ootheca is deposited in a secluded location. Interestingly, there is some transfer of nutrients from the female to the ootheca after it is formed. Eggs from ootheca that are prematurely removed from the female are not viable. Some species of cockroaches will carry the egg case until the larvae hatch.

Cockroaches have incomplete metamorphosis. Most cockroach larvae resemble wingless adults. Cockroaches have chewing mouthparts both as larvae and adults. Cockroaches often will regurgitate onto food before ingestion. This has the effect of partially digesting the food before it is ingested. Besides being disgusting, cockroaches can potentially ingest pathogens and spread them to food when they regurgitate. Cockroaches are known to harbor salmonella, a human pathogen. However, cockroaches are not efficient transmitters of disease, partly because the amount of regurgitant deposited is limited. Cockroaches can also carry filth on their bodies.

When I was a student at another university, cockroaches infested our building and offices. I quickly discovered that postage stamps left in my desk drawer would no longer stick to envelopes. The cockroaches were feeding on the glue on the stamps. This put me off licking stamps and envelopes.

Cockroach Allergy

Allergy is the most important medical problem related to cockroaches. Approximately one in five children in the United States have allergies to proteins in the cockroach droppings. Severe allergy can lead to asthma, an allergic reaction of the human respiratory system. Cockroach allergies are the #1 cause of asthma attacks resulting in hospitalization in urban U.S. cities. Recently developed programs use high vacuum and deep cleaning to remove cockroach allergens from infested buildings. However, sanitation and proper building maintenance to prevent large infestations in the first place are cheaper than remediation.

In The Ear

Of minor medical importance are cockroaches crawling in ears (unless it is your ear). In domiciles with large cockroach infestations, it is not uncommon for cockroaches to crawl in the ears of sleeping individuals. The medical profession is currently divided on best practice for cockroach removal from the ear. Some doctors suggest placing mineral oil in the ear to suffocate the cockroach, although this can be a slow process. Some doctors have tried lidocaine to anesthetize the cockroach before removal. In some instances the cockroach will respond by rapidly exiting the ear; in others the cockroach remains in the ear and is difficult to remove. Most problematic is the cockroach trying to escape the chemical by pushing its way through the eardrum. Simply thrusting forceps into the ear may cause the cockroach to move further into the ear canal. Doctors are still debating the best method for removing cockroaches from the ear.

Bionic Roaches?

Because cockroaches are very good at maneuvering through cracks and crevices, there is some interest in modifying cockroaches for use as "bio-robots." Potential uses for "bionic roaches" include crawling through earthquake rubble with a camera to search for victims, or slipping under doors on espionage surveillance (gives a new meaning to "bugging an office"). Roaches can be given electrical stimulation that so that roaches can be remotely manipulated to move a trackball and devices connected to the trackball.

Urban Ecology

Cockroaches can be an important part of the urban ecosystem. Large cities have sufficient garbage for cockroaches to eat. The cockroaches can be a major food source for rats. Large roach populations will support large rat populations. Rats eat the bodies of cockroaches but not the wings. Large piles of cockroach wings indicate rat-feeding sites. Controlling cockroaches is an important component of reducing rat populations in urban areas.

Cockroach Control

The most important part of cockroach control is sanitation. Elimination of food and water that can support cockroaches is necessary for effective control. Cockroaches need to drink water. In homes and businesses, water can be found in leaks around plumbing or toilets, in the evaporator pan under refrigerators and in dirty dishes stacked in a sink. Repair of leaking plumbing is important. Cleanliness, washing dishes in a timely manner, storing food in roach-proof containers, placing garbage in a roach-proof container, and emptying the garbage consistently are important sanitation steps.

In large apartment complexes, a single resident with dysfunctional cleaning habits can create a rapidly expanding cockroach population that overruns the entire building. Although walls separate apartments, cockroaches can easily move through holes in walls where utilities enter, such as around pipes, heating vents, and electrical conduits. It is not possible to seal an apartment against entry by cockroaches.

In these situations, tenants that practice even the best sanitation standards can have cockroach infestations. The cockroach problem must be addressed at the building level. Cockroach control requires enforcement of communal standards for cleanliness. In some states building managers have authority to evict tenants that contribute to a cockroach nuisance.

Insecticides

Insecticides can be useful for cockroach control and are most effective when combined with good sanitation efforts. Crack and crevice sprays were once the most popular method of treating for cockroaches but baits are used more frequently today. In crack and crevice spraying, insecticides are sprayed into cracks that harbor the cockroaches. Some insecticides have a "flushing action" that causes the cockroaches to leave the cracks. Many of these insecticides are neurotoxins that quickly immobilize the cockroaches, leaving them on their back with their legs in the air. The disadvantage to crack and crevice spray is exposure of building occupants to volatile insecticides.

In 2002, the U.S. EPA banned the use of certain insecticides (cholinesterase inhibitors) indoors because of concerns about long-term effects on residents. Some insecticides are unsafe to use indoors and their use is illegal. While these insecticides are very good at killing and controlling cockroach populations, they cause illness in people exposed to them. Contamination of buildings is a problem. This problem can be avoided by only dealing with professional, trained exterminators. Saving a few pennies on insect control can lead to huge remediation costs and much larger headaches.

The recent trend in cockroach control is to use baits instead of crack and crevice sprays. Cockroach insecticide is formulated with a bait food the cockroach will consume. The baits are applied to areas that people are unlikely to contact. Because the insecticides used in the baits are not volatile and people do not eat the baits, human exposure to the insecticide is reduced. Baits are commonly used in schools and public buildings to reduce the exposure of people to insecticide residues.

Purdue University is one of the recognized leaders in the control of urban pests including cockroaches. The first prototype indoor insecticide sprayer was developed at Purdue by a Purdue professor and two of his students. The sprayer was commercialized as the B&G Sprayer, still sold today.

Termites

Global Importance Of Termites

There are over 2,500 species of termites. Termites have a global distribution and great diversity. However, termites fare better under tropical conditions than temperate conditions. The numbers of individuals, numbers of species, and nest variety increase toward the equator.

Ecological Importance Of Termites

Termites have an important role in recycling the nutrients in dead wood. Dead trees decompose very slowly and termites speed the process. Termites chew dead wood into smaller pieces and provide a moist gut environment that aids in digestion. Termites contain symbionts in their guts that help digest the cellulose in wood.

Termite Evolution

Termites evolved from common ancestors of the wood-eating cockroach. Unlike termites, the wood-eating cockroach is not a social insect. The wood-eating cockroach requires several years to develop from larva to adult. Multiple generations can share the same log, but they are not social insects because they lack communal care of young.

In contrast, all termites live in colonies and are social insects. All termite species have communal care of young and a caste system.

Termite History

Termite fossils have been identified from the Cretaceous period about 130 mya. Termites are a much more recent group than their cockroach ancestors. Termites are placed in the Order Isoptera, which means "same" (iso) "wing" (ptera) in Latin. The wings of termites are about the same size and a similar shape. "Termite" is derived from a Latin term that means "wood worm." Like cockroaches, termites have chewing mouthparts, and incomplete metamorphosis.

Economic Importance

Termites are the most important urban pest in the United States. Termites cause structural damage and billions of dollars are spent annually on prevention, repair, treatment, and research into termite control.

Characteristics Of Termites

Termites live in large complex colonies. They are adapted to living underground and have cryptic habits that make them difficult to detect. Signs of a termite infestation in a human structure include damage or mud tubes. Termites construct mud tubes from particles of soil or wood that are glued together with feces, saliva, and other secretions. Mud tubes protect termites from desiccation and predation while they travel from their feeding sites to a source of water. Termites require a source of water or the colony will die. Blocking termite access to water is an important component of termite control.

Cellulose As A Nutrient

Cellulose is the primary structural component of trees and is the most abundant organic chemical in the world (by weight and volume). Cellulose is a carbohydrate that contains only carbon, hydrogen, and oxygen. It is not a source of amino acids or nitrogen that are needed for chitin and insect proteins. Dead trees do not contain many of the essential vitamins that animals need. The poor nutritional quality of dead trees does not encourage its utilization as food by animals. Very few organisms can digest cellulose. This is why dead trees (wood) persist for long periods.

Termite Digestion

Cellulose digestion is dependent on microorganisms (symbionts) harbored in the termite hindgut. Termite symbionts produce enzymes that metabolize cellulose (long sugar polymers) by releasing the individual sugars that make up the long cellulose molecules. The symbionts use the energy and fixed carbon from the cellulose metabolism to create nutrients (amino acids, lipids, and vitamins) that are important to both the symbionts and the termite.

The symbionts benefit from living in the termite gut. The gut provides a suitable environment for metabolism and the termites provide a constant supply of cellulose. The termites gain because the symbionts are capable of producing vitamins and other nutrients that are in low supply in the wood the termites eat as food. Termites would not be able to successfully consume wood if not for the symbionts. The symbionts are not capable of living on their own outside the termite gut.

Most insects that feed on low-quality food require longer development times than insects feeding on high quality food. Because they are social insects, adult termites can transfer additional nutrients to the young allowing them to grow faster than they would if they were not social.

Termite Society

Termites have a caste system with distinct division of labor, overlapping generations and cooperative care of offspring. Every termite species has one or more sterile castes.
Each colony has a single reproductive male and female.

Workers

Unlike the workers of ants, bees, and wasps, termite workers are both male and female. Hormones released by the king and queen suppress the reproductive systems of worker termites. If the queen termite dies, the hormones are no longer present and workers may become reproductives. Termite workers are responsible for the damage to human property. Workers forage for food, digest cellulose, feed and groom colony members, excavate galleries, build mud tubes, and patch broken tubes.

Soldiers

Soldiers are sterile males and females that have developed characters adapted to colony defense. Soldiers typically have heavily sclerotized head capsules and enlarged mandibles. Soldiers specialize in defense, are more aggressive than workers, and do not groom, feed, excavate tunnels, or build nests. Some termite species have soldiers with nozzles on their heads (nasutes) that secrete or spray noxious defensive chemicals.

Primary Reproductives (Alates)

Primary reproductives are called alates during their dispersal phase when they have wings. If environmental conditions are appropriate, alates will fly from the colony in large swarms to mate and start new colonies. The alates are commonly seen by homeowners and may be the first alert to the presence of termites.

A breeding pair of one male and female will select a site to start a new colony. The wings break off after they land. Flying termites and termites with rudimentary colonies are more vulnerable to predation than established colonies. The success rate for termite reproductives is low. However, successful individuals can live a long time. A termite queen can live up to 30 years and lay one egg every 15 seconds. How many eggs can one queen lay in a lifetime?

Termite Or Ant?

Termites are often called "white ants," because of their white color. Some ants have winged reproductives that swarm adding to the confusion. Termites have two wings of the same size and shape and lack a constriction of the abdomen. Flying ants typically have hind wings that are smaller than their fore wings and ants have a constriction in the abdomen.

Termites consume wood and their galleries are typically filled with particles of detritus. Because termites eat and digest the wood, they do not leave piles of sawdust outside the tunnels. Termites commonly forage below ground or inside mud tubes. The termite nest is decentralized and moves often.

Carpenter ants nest in wood but do not consume the wood. Carpenter ant galleries have smooth sandpapered appearance. Carpenter ants carry wood particles outside the nest to dump them. Carpenter ants are nocturnal above ground foragers and their nests are often made in water-damaged wood.

Termite Foraging

Termites can forage for distances of many meters. Foraging occurs 24 hours a day and is random, but concentrated. Termites utilize trail pheromones, odors that are laid by the sternal gland. Trail pheromone is laid from the food back to the nest. The trail is re-enforced by each returning forager.

Termites share their food by trophallaxis, a mutual exchange of secretions and liquid food between individuals. Trophallaxis is a means of feeding the soldiers, reproductives, and immatures. Trophallaxis helps to maintain consistent colony odor. Gut symbionts are transferred among termites by trophallaxis.

Mutual Grooming

Termites are noted for mutual grooming. Grooming removes soil, bacteria, fungi, and parasites from termites. Grooming helps keep the colony sanitary and disease free.

Cuticular Hydrocarbons

Cuticular hydrocarbons are lipids that are secreted onto the outside of the termite cuticle Cuticular hydrocarbons are responsible for nest mate recognition. Nest mates share the same set of cuticle chemicals and emit the "nest odor." Intruders lack the proper chemicals and can be recognized because they lack nest odor. Nest mate recognition is similar in termites and ants.

Termite Inspections.

Termite inspections are an important part of home buying in the United States. Most lenders will require that a home be inspected for termites and termite colonies eliminated before they will lend money. A termite inspector determines if termites are present or not. Signs of infestation can include mud tubes, damage, termite wings, or live insects. If signs of termite damage or mud tubes are present, the inspector must determine if it is active or an old infestation.

The termite inspector must distinguish termite damage from damage by other insects, vertebrates, wood rot, or moisture damage. Some recently developed inspection aids include termite inspecting dogs, infrared technology, thermal imaging, microwave detection devices, and acoustic technology.

Termite inspectors must be prepared to enter dark, dirty, and potentially dangerous areas of a structure. Inspection devices include a flashlight and personal protective equipment such as a dust mask, hard hat, kneepads, boots, coveralls, and gloves. Knives, awls, and hammers may be used to probe the wood for tunnels. Inspectors must write a report and may require measuring tape and graph paper to indicate and mark the location of termite colonies and/or damage for future elimination.

Environmental factors that influence termite infestations include the type of vegetation, climate, rainfall, food availability, and moisture. Environmental factors determine which termite species can inhabit an areas. For example, some species of termites are best adapted to sandy soils, whereas other termites are best adapted to clay soils. Some termite species are adapted to cold temperatures, whereas other species are limited to areas that are above freezing year round.

Termite Pest Management

Termite management includes cultural and sanitation methods. It is good building practice to avoid contact between wood and soil. Direct contact provides easy access to the wood for termites living in the soil. High moisture areas, which encourage termites, should be eliminated by adjusting the slope of the landscape. Physical barriers, termite shields, sand barriers, and chemical treatments can all prevent termites from damaging a structure.

Chemical Control

The two most popular chemical control methods for termites are a liquid insecticide barrier or a baiting program. The liquid barrier is an insecticide that is placed around the foundation of the house. Termites that approach are killed by the insecticide in the barrier zone before they can harm the house. Liquid barriers have a limited lifetime, but they are effective as long as the insecticide is present.

Baiting programs utilize traps to detect termite colonies. If termite feeding is detected, the less expensive monitoring bait is replaced by a more expensive bait containing a slow acting insecticide. The termites will carry the slow-acting insecticide back to the nest where it will be spread by trophallaxis and the colony will be eliminated. The insecticide must act slowly so it does not kill the worker before it can return to the nest with the insecticide.

The barrier method requires less monitoring after the treatment. However, the chemical cost is more expensive and the potential for environmental contamination is greater. Bait methods use far less pesticide (or none at all) so they reduce environmental risk and the cost of chemicals is less. However, the monitoring costs are much higher. Currently both methods are in use and the cost is comparable.

Some areas are very susceptible to termite damage. Termites threaten numerous historical buildings and our cultural heritage. Infestations have been found and eliminated from several buildings on the Purdue campus.

Dragonflies And Damselflies

Dragonflies and damselflies first appeared in the Devonian over 360 million years ago (mya). They are considered the oldest surviving group of flying insects. There are numerous fossil wings in coal deposits. Some of the wings of fossil dragonfly-like insects are far larger than extant species, with wing spans over half a meter. However, many of the dragonfly wings are similar to extant species and clearly have changed little over 300 million years.

Dragonfly Larvae

Dragonfly larvae are aquatic and have special modifications for breathing underwater. Inside their rectum, dragonflies have gills that exchange oxygen and carbon dioxide with the water. Dragonfly larvae use muscles to pump water in and out. They are also capable of rapidly expelling water in order to escape predators. Rapidly forcing water out of the narrow opening at the end of the abdomen creates a jet action that propels the insects rapidly forward.

Dragonflies are predaceous as adults and larvae. Dragonfly larvae remain motionless on the bottom of a lake or stream and wait for prey to come within reach. Prey items are typically insects, but may include fish and tadpoles that are small enough to handle.

The larvae have a special extendable labium (mouthpart). The labium has a grasper at the end of a long hinged arm. At rest the grasper covers the mouth like a mask and is called a labial mask. When prey gets close, the labium extends in an instant and the grasper captures the prey. Then, the labium flexes at the hinge to bring the captured prey to the mouth where it can be chewed into pieces by the other mouthparts of the larva and swallowed.

Dragonfly Adults

Dragonfly adults are also predaceous but capture prey on the wing. Dragonfly legs have long spines that form a basket. Dragonflies overtake other flying insects and trap them in the basket formed by their legs. Sometimes insects are impaled on the leg spines. The captured prey are brought to the mouth and eaten. Adult dragonflies are important predators of mosquitoes and other flying insects.

Male dragonflies are territorial and fight each other for the best spots. Male dragonflies can often be seen smashing into each other in flight. Sometimes both tumble to the ground and continue thrashing until the loser bolts. Males can become even more aggressive in the presence of a female and hotly compete for mates.

Mating in dragonflies takes place in flight. Prior to mating, the male deposits sperm in a sperm pouch near the front of the abdomen. The appendages at the end of the abdomen are used for grasping the female between the head and thorax. The female collects sperm from the pouch with the end of her abdomen. Males and females fly in tandem while laying eggs in the water. Contact between the tip of the female abdomen and the water can create drag while flying. The male provides additional lift to prevent the female from falling into the water and hastens her escape from potential fish predators.

Damselflies

Damselflies are closely related to dragonflies. Dragonflies have a stouter body than damselflies and the larvae have different mechanisms for breathing. Damselfly larvae have gills on the ends of their abdomen. Like dragonflies, damselflies are predators.

Mayflies

Mayflies are an ancient group. Some mayfly fossils are older than 360 million years. Unlike the dragonflies, mayflies are herbivorous or feed on dead organic matter as larvae. Adults live only long enough to mate and do not feed.

Mayflies are the only insects known to molt from one stage with wings to a second winged stage. Mayfly larvae are aquatic. Before the molt to the first winged form, aquatic mayfly larvae swim to the surface and emerge as subimagos. The subimago is a poor flyer but can get from the water to shore. Once on shore, the mayfly molts to a true adult that is a better flyer. Mayflies live for only a short time as adults and do not feed. Adults mate, lay eggs and die.

A common mayfly strategy to avoid predation is emergence in large swarms. This "predator satiation" reduces the fraction of adults that are eaten. In Lake St Clair near Detroit, massive mayfly emergences appear on Doppler radar. Mayflies can coat large parts of the countryside for a couple of days, and then just as suddenly disappear. They are called "mayflies" because they emerge in May.

Environmental Monitors

Some mayfly species are extremely sensitive to environmental conditions especially pollution. The presence of certain species of mayfly larvae indicates that the water is good quality. The absence of those species can indicate the presence of pollutants or bad water conditions.

A. Dragonfly resting with wings horizontal. Dragonflies lack the ability to fold their wings over their back like most insects.   B. Familiar Bluet, a common damselfly in Indiana.   C. Ebony Jewel Wing Damselfly. Damselflies and dragonflies are predators as both larvae and adults. The larvae of both dragonflies and damselflies live underwater.

Chapter 9 Study Questions

Beetles

1. What does the name Coleoptera mean?

2. When do beetles first appear in the fossil record?

3. Describe the movement of beetle wings during flight?

4. Why are there more species of beetle than any other insect?

5. What types of diseases are spread by beetles?

6. What do lady beetles eat?

7. How do fireflies produce light?

8. What is a femme fatale firefly?

9. Why did the city of Enterprise, Alabama erect a statue to the boll weevil?

10. How do stag beetles use their large mandibles?

11. What do sexton beetles eat?

12. How do tiger beetles get their name?

13. How do bombardier beetles produce hot liquid for defense?

Lepidoptera

1. What does the name Lepidoptera mean?

2. What are the differences between butterflies and moths?

3. How are iridescent colors on butterfly wings produce?

4. What is Aposematism?

5. Why do butterflies puddle?

6. How do loopers move?

7. How do most moths find mates?

8. How is silk produced?

9. What are some economically important Lepidoptera?

Flies

1. What does the name Diptera mean?

2. When do Diptera first appear in the fossil record?

3. What causes mosquito bites?

4. How do mosquitoes acquire and transmit disease?

5. Where do mosquito larvae live and how is that related to mosquito control?

6. List the primary causative disease agent and the primary vector for:
   a. Malaria

b.   Encephalitis

c.   Yellow fever

d.   Elephantiasis

e.   Lyme disease

f.   Leishmaniasis

7. What flies are important pests of wheat?

Fleas

1. What is the most common flea found on pets?

2. Where do cat flea larvae develop?

3. What fleas are involved in bubonic plague?

4. What are buboes?

5. How did fleas and the plague affect the history of thirteenth-century Asia?

6. How did fleas and the plague affect the European colonization of North America?

Hymenoptera

1. What does the name Hymenoptera mean?

2. Why is the abdominal constriction of Hymenoptera important to parasitoids?

3. What wasp makes its nest out of mud?

4. What are the most common wasps that visit picnics in the fall?

Honey Bees

5. What do honey bees eat?

6. What is propolis?

7. Where do bees get beeswax?

8. When were bees first domesticated?

9. How do honey bees mate?

10. What is a waggle dance?

11. How do bees sting?

12. What are killer bees?

Ants
13. Which weighs more: All the ants? Or all the mammals?

14. What sex are worker ants?

15. What type of ants don't construct a nest?

16. What are propaganda substances?

17. How do ants recognize nest mates?

18. At what age can ants be made into "slaves" by slave making ants?

19. What is stigmergy?

20. What are the 3 basic processes that social insects use to alter their environment?

21. What features of ant pheromone make it a good for communicating the location of food?

22. What similarities are there between Internet search engines and the ant trail pheromone system?

True Bugs and Relatives

1. When do the true bugs first appear in the fossil record?

2. Why are bed bugs difficult to control?

3. Are bed bugs an indicator of poor sanitation?

4. What true bug can walk on water?

5. What is honeydew?

6. What features distinguish the dog day cicada from the periodic cicada?

7. Where do cicadas feed?

8. Where do periodic cicadas lay eggs?

9. Where do head lice lay their eggs?

10. How are pubic lice transmitted?

11. What factors promote book lice infestations in libraries?

Orthoptera

1. What does the name Orthoptera mean?

2. What features distinguish katydids from grasshoppers?

3. What do crickets eat?

4. What are plague locusts?

Phasmida

1. What features and behaviors help stick insects avoid detection?

2. Describe the process that leads leaf insects to closely resemble their host plants?

Stoneflies

1. Where do stonefly larvae live?

2. How did the winter stonefly get its name?

Earwigs

1. What feature distinguishes earwigs?

2. Do earwigs commonly crawl in the ears of people?

Mantids

1. What features distinguish mantids?

2. How do female mantids attract mates?

3. How is mimicry important to mantids?

4. Will female mantids eat male mantids?

Cockroaches

1. When do cockroaches first appear in the fossil record?

2. How many species of cockroaches have been described?

3. How many species of cockroaches are pests?

4. What is the most important medical problem created by cockroaches?

5. What is the best way to remove a cockroach from the ear canal?

6. What is the most important factor in cockroach control?

7. What changes and trends have been made to cockroach control in the last decade?

Termites

1. What is the ecological role of termites?

2. What is the caste structure of termite colonies?

3. Are workers male or female?

4. What are mud tubes?

5. What features help termites digest cellulose?

6. What features distinguish termites and ants?

7. What is trophallaxis and why is it important for cellulose digestion?

8. How do termites recognize nest mates?

9. What steps can be taken during building a house to prevent termite damage?

10. What are the two common methods of protecting a structure from nearby termites?

Dragonflies and Damselflies

1. When do dragonflies first appear in the fossil record?

2. Where do dragonfly and damselfly larvae live?

3. What do larvae eat and what specializations do they have for feeding?

4. What do adult dragonflies eat?

Mayflies

1. When do mayflies first appear in the fossil record?

2. What is unique about winged stages of mayflies?

3. Why how are mayflies used to monitor environmental quality?

Chapter 10

Invasive Species and Emerald Ash Borer

Geographical Distribution of Species

Species have a geographic distribution. Not all species occur in all locations. For example, you would not expect to find the same species of plants and animals (including insects) that live in Indiana if you traveled to Australia. Oceans, deserts, mountains, or ice caps can all be barriers to movement of species. These barriers have ensured that some species of insects are confined to their current locations for long periods of time, often millions of years.

Human Effects

The activities of humans can provide exotic species with transportation past natural barriers. Some introductions of exotic species are intentional. For instance, the gypsy moth was brought to North America from Europe in an attempt to breed a better silk moth. However, many exotic insects are introduced unintentionally. The trade in manufactured goods among continents has expanded greatly in the last century. The expansion of trade gives many species more opportunity for unintentional transport from their native location to novel exotic locations. The United States has received many unintentional introductions of species. Other countries have been recipients of unintentional introductions from the United States (including the introduction of Colorado potato beetle and corn rootworm from the United States into Europe).

Species appearing in a new location for the first time are called exotic species (in that location). Exotic species can be defined as species not native or endemic to an area. Introductions can come from across the planet or across town. Most often with exotic insects, the introductions come from long distances past natural barriers. The majority of exotic species are ill adapted to the environmental conditions in the new location. For this reason, most introduced species fail to thrive and disappear without establishing a permanent population.

Exotic species that rapidly increase in abundance and distribution are called invasive species. Invasive species establish permanent populations, thrive in their new location, may displace native species and may become pests. Invasive species can be plants (purple loosestrife, kudzu, and garlic mustard), animals (starlings, zebra mussels, Japanese beetle, common carp, or soybean aphid) or microorganisms and pathogens such as West Nile virus.

Approximately 1 in every 7 exotic species becomes invasive. The cost to the United States in damage, control, and remediation was estimated to be more than $100 billion per year in 2006. Invasive species have a negative impact on nearly half of the species on the endangered species list. Invasive species have important effects on agriculture, biodiversity, ecosystem quality and health, quality and quantity of natural resources, international trade and human health.

Over 6 billion tons of goods worth more than $6 trillion were transported in international trade in the year 2000. It would be too costly to inspect the large quantity of trade goods in detail. In the United States, less than 2 percent of trade goods are thoroughly inspected.

Some types of products or their packing materials are responsible for transport of damaging insect species. For example, solid wood packing material was used in the transport of more than half of the trade goods imported into or exported from the United States in 1999. A significant percentage of solid wood may be contaminated with insects. Failure to remove bark completely from the wood may increase contamination by wood boring insects. Treating wood with heat or insecticides prior to shipping can decrease the insect contamination. Such treatments are currently required but compliance is an issue.

If wood used for packing contains wood boring insects then those insects will be transported along with the trade goods. When the trade goods arrive at their destination, they are unpacked and the wood discarded, often in large piles. If wood-boring insects survive the transportation process, they can disperse from the piles of wood packing material and colonize wood or trees in their new location.

As a result of trade, many of the 500 species of forest trees in the United States are infested with exotic species of insects. About 4000 exotic species of insects have become permanently established in the United States. Damage to trees ranges from minimal to extinction.

Emerald Ash Borer, A Case Study

The Emerald Ash Borer (EAB) belongs to family of wood boring beetles (Buprestidae). Buprestid beetles are common around the world. The beetle larvae feed on plants, typically, the vascular tissue of trees. Trees take water and minerals from the soil and transport it to the leaves. This is done with their vascular (or transport) tissue. The larvae of many buprestids feed on this vascular tissue that is located just under the bark. If the vascular tissue is disrupted in a complete circle around the trunk or stem, then the tree is labeled "girdled." Girdling prevents water and other nutrients from moving past the "girdle" so those tissues will die. Even if the vascular tissue is not girdled, lesser disruptions can negatively affect the tree. Vascular disruption can cause parts of the tree to weaken, increase susceptibility to other insect pests and diseases and lead to premature death.

The EAB, a native of Asia, feeds on Asian species of ash. In Asia, ash trees have evolved tolerance to the EAB. EAB will damage Asian ash trees and kill weakened trees. However, EAB does not kill healthy Asian ash trees. The larvae develop under the bark of trees, feeding on the vascular tissues. The larvae pupate in the wood. Later, the EAB emerge as adults, and disperse.

Probably during the 1990s, the EAB was transported to North America (most likely in solid wood packing material). The EAB established in the Detroit area and was first detected in 2002. Since its establishment, the EAB has killed over 17 million North American ash trees.

Ash trees in North American have no historical exposure to EAB and are killed within 1 to 3 years by heavy populations. Mortality is 100 percent. This is a concern because ash trees are a valuable resource used for furniture and other wood products. The United States has about 8 billion forest ash trees. There are approximately 147 million ash trees in Indiana forests and another 3 to 4 million ash trees in Indiana urban areas. About 6 percent of forest trees in Indiana are ash. The EAB has the potential to kill 100 percent of these ash trees. What would be the impact if all the ash trees in Indiana died suddenly? What can we do to stop the EAB or at least slow its effects?

We know that the EAB, left to its own means, moves less than 1 kilometer per year (about ¼ to ½ mile). However, the EAB larvae are easily moved in ash products such as firewood, logs, and nursery stock. The spread of EAB could be slowed if infested materials were not transported. However, EAB larvae are difficult to detect because it lives under the tree bark where it is out of sight and difficult to inspect. It is difficult to distinguish infested from uninfested wood. Therefore, transport of all wood products from areas infested with EAB is banned to slow the spread of the pest.

Quarantines. Quarantines are legal restrictions on transport. It is illegal to transport wood products from quarantined areas. Violators are subject to substantial fines. White County (just north of Lafayette and Tippecanoe County) is infested with EAB. Nursery stock, firewood, and other wood products cannot be transported from White County. The EAB in White County was first detected in a campground near Indiana Beach resort. How did it most likely get there?

Where Is EAB?

Currently EAB is in several neighboring states including Michigan, Ohio, and Illinois. As of 2009, it had spread to Wisconsin, Pennsylvania, New York, West Virginia, Virginia, Missouri, Kentucky, and Maryland. EAB may already be in other states because it is difficult to detect until damage is visible, perhaps a period of several years. Michigan, where the infestation probably originated, has the most infested area. The USDA and state agencies are currently monitoring the spread of emerald ash borer. The "Pest Tracker" website publishes up to date maps of the location of emerald ash borer and other invasive pests.

EAB has been found in several Indiana counties. There are statewide inspections to identify new infestations of EAB. Detection will remain difficult until effective traps are developed for EAB. Unfortunately, an attractant for EAB that is as potent as gypsy moth pheromone is not available. EAB does not orient to pheromones from long distances as the gypsy moth does, making development of a pheromone trap unlikely. Crude methods of surveying for EAB include placing damaged ash saplings as "trap trees" to attract EAB. This is an expensive and time-consuming method. Entomologists are researching better methods of surveying for EAB.

Globalization of pest problems

Eradication of invasive species can be expensive, difficult or even impossible. The focus must be on preventing the importation of exotic species. Invasive species can cause much environmental and economic damage. Containing the damage is expensive and may be impossible once the pest is established. Laws and regulations to prevent export and good compliance with the rules are the most cost-effective way (and sometimes the only way) to prevent damage from harmful invasive species.

A. A healthy ash tree. B. D-shaped exit holes are made by emerging adult emerald ash borers. C. Galleries are made by emerald ash borer feeding just under the bark. Galleries increase

(*continued on page 181*)

Chapter 10 • Invasive Species and Emerald Ash Borer

Chapter 10 Study Questions

1. What is the difference between an exotic species and an invasive species?

2. What factor has led to the importation of wood boring pests from around the world?

3. What factors make the Emerald Ash Borer (EAB) such a devastating pest?

4. What factors make the EAB difficult to treat and impossible to eradicate?

(plate caption *continued*)

in size with each larval stage.   D. Wooden pallet used in shipment of goods. Wood used for export should be stripped of its bark and treated with heat or pesticide to kill insects. Emerald ash borer probably came to the US in solid wood packing material.

5. What measures should homeowners take in response to the EAB threat?

6. What are quarantines and how are they used for EAB management?

7. Why is it so difficult to stop the importation of pest insects entirely?

Chapter 11

Managing Insect Pests

Integrated Pest Management

The vast majority of insects are benign and have little interaction with people. However, some insects cause significant damage to the human health, crops, and possessions. Control is necessary. Attempts at insect control can have negative as well as positive consequences. It is important to minimize the harm and be as selective in our insect control as possible. Integrated pest management (IPM) is a strategy to effectively manage insect pests while minimizing costs and negative effects. To do this, we need to answer the following questions:

1. What pests need to be controlled?
2. When is control necessary?
3. Where is control necessary?
4. How is the best way to control a pest?
5. What is the best way to balance the economic costs and benefits of pest control with protection of human health and the environment?
6. Can the system be improved?

Integrated pest management practice requires knowledge of pests and populations and utilizes all pest control techniques. In IPM, pest presence and populations are monitored. Insecticides are only used if it is determined that there is a net economic benefit.

Economic Injury Levels

Many crops can sustain some feeding damage without harming yield or reducing the value of the crop. For example, consider a grain crop that yields 150 bushels per acre with no insects. Suppose that 20 insects per plant will reduce the yield from 150 to 120 bushels per acre. Is it cost effective to control the insects?

If the grain sells for $3 per bushel and insecticide treatment costs $15 per acre would the farmer earn more money by treating the crop?

Suppose that 10 insects per plant reduces the yield by 4 bushels per acre. At $3 per bushel, would the farmer come out ahead if it cost $15 to treat the crop with insecticide? (Do the math to find the answer).

Agricultural entomologists research the relationship between insect populations and the extent of the damage and loss of yield. Once the relationship between the number of insects and loss of yield is determined, the farmer can monitor the insect population and calculate whether or not it is cost effective to treat the crop based on expected crop prices.

There is a level of pest population where the costs of controlling the pest are equal to the amount of damage caused by the pest. This level is called the economic injury level (EIL). If a pest population is increasing and approaching the EIL, then it is economically beneficial to control the pest to prevent its population from exceeding the economic injury level. If the pest population is below the economic injury level and not increasing, controlling the pest would cost more than the benefit of a slightly higher yield. Once the economic injury level is determined, growers can monitor pest populations and use EIL to determine when to treat. Knowing the EIL allows the farmer to avoid unnecessary insecticide treatments. Eliminating unnecessary treatments saves money and minimizes the negative effects of insect control efforts.

Some insects may cause minor damage but never exceed the economic injury level. Those insects do not need to be controlled. Only insects that are capable of exceeding the economic injury level need to be controlled. Those potential pest insects only need to be controlled when populations are increasing and threaten to exceed the economic injury level.

Where Should Insects Be Treated?

It may be possible to treat a pest in several locations, but some of those treatments may be more effective than others. For example, it is possible to control mosquito larvae by treating their breeding areas. It is also possible to treat mosquito adults by fogging. In most cases it is far more effective to treat the larval populations. Larval treatments typically have fewer negative environmental impacts than fogging for adults. Therefore, mosquito control programs focus primarily on controlling the mosquito larvae. However, there are instances when incidents of mosquito-vectored diseases are high and it is desirable to control mosquitoes in both locations.

Measuring Pest Populations

Entomologists study insects to determine when and where insects are likely to be present. Insects (and the embryos inside eggs) grow slowly or not at all if temperatures are low and grow more rapidly when temperatures are optimal. Insect emergence can often be predicted by measuring temperatures and calculating heat units called degree days. Degree days can be used to alert the grower when to monitor for specific pests. A typical degree day calculation uses the base temperature (the temperature, below which no growth or development occurs) and the average temperature. The number of degree days in a single day is the average temperature minus the base temperature. Degree days accumulate and the accumulated degree days are calculated by summing the degree days for all the days that the average temperature is above the base temperature. Degree days are commonly used by farmers to determine when they should begin looking for insects or insect damage in their crops.

Traps are commonly used for field monitoring of pest populations. Insect population information is used to make decisions about whether or not the pest will exceed the EIL. Entomologists study the behavior of insects and design traps so that they maximize the capture of the pest insects and not unimportant insects. In the least sophisticated applications, the presence or absence of pest insects in the trap alerts the farmer to take steps to further monitor the insect populations. In more sophisticated applications, the number of insects in a trap are used to estimate the insect population or the likelihood of damage exceeding economic injury level. In these special cases, whenever the number of pests in a trap exceed a threshold, treatment is advised.

When traps provide incomplete or inconclusive information about the need to treat a pest, techniques such as direct observation or other sampling methods such as visual counts or the use of nets may be necessary. However, these techniques are usually more time consuming than trapping methods. Effective traps can save considerable labor and contribute to lower costs.

IPM Tools

There are multiple methods for managing insects that vary in cost and effectiveness. Integrated pest management philosophy includes the evaluation of all available techniques and choosing those that best fit the system. In many instances, insecticides are the most economical means of controlling insects. However, in some cases, insecticides are not always necessary and other methods of insect control may be preferred or the most economic method.

Biological Control

Biological control is using natural enemies, biological organisms such as insects and diseases to control pests. An example of biological control is the use of the Vedalia beetle to control the cottony cushion scale on citrus. Citrus is a crop that is not native to the United States. The cottony cushion scale (a scale insect,) was inadvertently introduced to the United States and was damaging the citrus industry. The USDA sent an entomologist to Australia where he found that the cottony cushion scale was controlled by Vedalia beetle. The Vedalia beetle was brought to the United States where it successfully established and has controlled the cottony cushion scale ever since. The Vedalia beetle was far more effective for control of the scale than other methods available at the time. Once established, the beetle is cost free.

Not all biological control efforts are as successful as the Vedalia beetle. However, successful efforts can have huge benefits with minimal costs. There is some concern about negative impacts of importing natural enemies. The Asian Lady beetle was imported into the United States to control aphid pests. However, large numbers of the beetles will invade homes in the fall in search of an overwintering site, to the annoyance of many homeowners. In other cases, natural enemies may affect insect species in addition to the pest. Important ecological balances could be upset. For this reason, the biology of potential biological control agents is studied to avoid importation of insects that will cause problems.

Plant Resistance

Plant resistance involves breeding plants that tolerate or deter insect damage. Plants may produce defensive chemicals that deter feeding by insects or have physical features that limit or prevent insect feeding. Some plant varieties may be better able to compensate for insect damage. Using varieties of plants that are resistant to insects can reduce or eliminate the need for insecticides or other methods of insect control.

Humans have been breeding plants that are used for food and fiber since the beginning of agriculture over ten thousand years ago. All agricultural civilizations use plant breeders to improve the nutritional and agronomic traits (including insect resistance) of their crops. The Incas of South

America used sophisticated techniques for identifying resistant varieties of crop plants long before contact with Europeans. They bred some of the important food plants that we grow today such as the potato and tomato.

Scientific agriculture uses sophisticated plant breeding techniques. Breeding for insect resistance requires cooperation between agronomists and entomologists. Entomologists identify plant varieties that are less damaged by insects. Plant breeders breed the important insect resistance characteristics into the plants. The USDA has an important wheat-breeding program at Purdue to release wheat varieties with resistance to the Hessian fly. This program saves wheat growers in the United States millions of dollars per year and eliminates the need to treat vast numbers of wheat fields with expensive insecticides.

Genetically Engineered Plants

In the past, plant breeders have relied on traits that were identified within the species of the crop plant. It was not possible to easily transfer genes from one organism to another. Decades of basic research on DNA and biochemistry have led to the development of techniques for the transfer of genes among organisms. Through genetic engineering, it is possible to create plants resistant to insects and other pests. The most common gene used for insect resistance is a gene from the bacteria, *Bacillus thuringiensis*. The bacteria produces a protein, Bt, that is toxic to some insects but non-toxic to people and livestock. Most Bt proteins only kill certain groups of insects. For instance, some Bt toxins only kill caterpillars; some only kill beetles, etc. None of the Bt toxins is harmful to people. People digest the Bt protein as we would any other non-toxic plant protein. Plant breeders have been able to clone the gene for the Bt protein from bacteria and "genetically engineer" it into the DNA of crop plants. The genetically engineered plants will produce the Bt protein. The Bt protein protects the plants from insect damage but the plants are still edible by humans and livestock.

Cultural Control

Cultural control is the control of pests by eliminating resources such as alternative plant hosts, over wintering sites and habitat. Cultural control includes plowing to eliminate weeds, actively removing breeding sites (water where mosquitoes develop, for instance) and crop rotation. Some successful examples of the use of cultural controls are wireworms in potato, rootworms in corn, and pink bollworm in cotton.

Wireworms are beetle larvae that feed on the roots of grass. If potatoes are planted in grassy fields the wireworms may also feed on the potatoes and damage the tubers. However, female wireworms will only lay eggs in fields that contain grass. By removing all grass from potato fields, wireworms will not be present to damage the potatoes. In this case cultural control is the most effect method to prevent wireworm damage.

Crop rotation is a form of cultural control by alternately planting host and non-host crops. Historically, crop rotation has been used to control corn rootworm (the number one economic pest in Indiana). The corn rootworm adults lay their eggs in corn fields in fall. If the corn field is planted to corn the next spring, the rootworms will hatch and damage the corn. If the corn field is rotated to soybeans the next year, the hatching rootworms will starve because they cannot eat soybeans. The rootworms lay few eggs in soybean fields. If soybean fields are rotated to corn the next spring, the corn will not be damaged because of the lack of rootworms.

Chapter 11 • Managing Insect Pests

Insect pests can sometimes defeat cultural control methods. Crop rotation in much of the Midwest is becoming less effective because some strains of rootworms will lay eggs in soybean as well as corn fields. If large numbers of eggs are laid in soybean fields, crop rotation will not effectively control corn rootworm.

Tillage is another form of cultural control that exposes insect pests to elements and removes weeds that may provide alternative hosts for the insects. There is a trend away from tillage in the fall because tillage can increase soil erosion by wind and water. However tillage is an important insect control practice. Pink bollworm control in cotton is a good example of using tillage for pest control. In the late fall, pink bollworm larvae burrow into the stems of cotton plants where they will overwinter. By establishing dates when all cotton in an area must be harvested and plowed, the overwintering larvae in a large area can be destroyed and minimize the pest population in the crop the following year.

Insect Control Devices

There are a number of devices marketed for pest control purposes. These devices vary in their effectiveness. It is difficult for consumers to find information on the effectiveness of these devices. Some work as advertised. Others may catch or kill insects but do little to control the pest or prevent damage, and some do not work at all. This section reviews some of the common devices with comments on their effectiveness.

Bug Zappers

Many are familiar with the crackle created when an insect collides with the electronic grid of a bug zapper. Bug zappers do kill insects. However most of the insects that they kill are not mosquitoes that might bite but harmless insects that contact the grid. Do bug zappers eliminate mosquito bites? Unfortunately, bug zappers typically kill only a small percentage of the insects (primarily mosquitoes) their users wish to control. It is possible through the use of lures such as octenol and carbon dioxide to increase the effectiveness of bug zappers for controlling female mosquitoes. However, none of the devices are as effective as an insect repellent containing DEET.

When insects contact the electric grid of a bug zapper, the energy from the electricity causes the insect to heat rapidly. The liquid inside a small insect may boil and cause the insect to explode. This can send a shower of insect parts in the vicinity of the bug zapper. Bug zappers are restricted from use in restaurants and areas where food is prepared. This is to prevent the contamination of the food with insect parts.

Foggers and Vapors

Citronella is marginally effective at repelling mosquitoes. Studies have shown that mosquitoes will avoid a citronella odor plume. However, people standing just to the edge of the citronella plume are still bitten. It is not possible to saturate an area with citronella completely enough to give effective mosquito control. Citronella candles can work, but only if you are standing next to one.

Backyard foggers are becoming more popular. Fogging can be effective as long as the insecticide is in the air as an aerosol. However, the insecticide dissipates within a couple of hours after which it is not effective. Under windy conditions, the aerosol can drift off site and dissipate even faster. Fogging when people are present exposes them to unwanted insecticide. This limits the usefulness of fogging.

Insect Traps

Entomologists primarily use traps for the detection of insect pests. Although there have been numerous attempts to use traps to control pest insects, these attempts typically fall short of the desired goal. A number of traps are marketed to the homeowner. Most of these traps are effective for detecting pests. Rarely are they effective for pest control

Indian meal moth traps. Indian meal moth traps are open-end paperboard boxes with glue on the inside surface. Indian meal moth traps are marketed with a pheromone lure to attract moths. These traps can fit neatly in a cupboard and can be checked to see if Indian meal moths are present.

The primary utility of these traps is to alert the homeowner to the presence of infested stored goods. Only male moths are attracted to the trap and captured, so the traps do very little to control the population. If moths are present, the homeowner should thoroughly clean the cupboard and inspect any boxes that contain flour or stored grains. In practice, the traps do little more than serve as a reminder to inspect cupboards and discard food that is too old. However, the traps can be fun and educational for the kids and be used for interesting science fair projects. In larger operations such as grocery stores and food warehouses, Indian meal moth traps can improve sanitation and elimination of contaminated products. In these situations, the traps alert the management that a pest population is present somewhere in the facility and a thorough search is warranted.

Fly paper works to kill and control flies, but is messy. New sticky strips are available to place on windows. These traps use light to attract flies that become stuck to the glue. However, most people consider them messy, dislike the sticky glue and the unsightly insects stuck to the fly paper. The primary users of fly paper are home gardeners who get fruit fly infestations on their tomatoes. The fly paper catches a lot of flies but does not eliminate the problem.

Glue Traps

Glue traps are available for a variety of insects including large insects such as crickets. Glue traps are simple to use but minimally effective for insect control. Large glue traps are available for pests as large as mice. Glue traps are an alternative to wire spring traps and can be baited to attract mice and rats. Compared to the wire spring traps, the glue traps are messier and take longer to kill the rodent. Effective wire spring traps will kill the rodent instantaneously. Rodents can harbor viruses and other diseases. It is best to handle traps containing dead rodents with gloves and to dispose of the trap along with the rodent.

Cockroach Traps

Pest control professionals will sometimes use sticky cards to trap cockroaches. The cards are placed near cracks and crevices that can harbor cockroaches. The traps are an indication of how well the treatments are working and what areas need more treatment. These traps are available to homeowners. They do trap and kill cockroaches. However, they typically only trap a small fraction of the population and add little to population control

Ant Baits

The ant bait stations can be effective in controlling and eliminating ant populations. Ant bait stations are typically plastic containers that enclose bait laced with insecticide. Entrance holes allow ants to forage and feed on the bait. Baits used to control ants are typically slow acting. This allows the foragers to return to the nest with the insecticide and spread the insecticide to other members of the colony. This method can eliminate an ant colony and the foragers.

Ant baits should not be used in conjunction with insecticide sprays or other treatments. Spraying ants kills those workers in the house that contact the spray and is not effective at eliminating the nest. Since the goal is to get foragers to carry as much of the insecticide as possible back to the nest, killing the foragers with sprays is counterproductive.

Termite Traps

Termite traps work on a similar principle to the ant baits. Termite traps are an alternative control method to spraying a barrier of insecticide on the soil next to a structure. Termite traps are plastic containers that are placed in the soil and baited with paper. The termite traps are used by professional services and not directly by homeowners. The professionals inspect the traps routinely. If a paper monitoring bait has termites, the bait is replaced with termite control bait that contains high concentrations of a slow-acting insecticide. The termite foragers carry the insecticide back to their colony and the colony is eliminated. Termite traps and the service contract are comparable to the cost of a barrier treatment. The traps are effective and a way to use less insecticide.

Japanese Beetle Traps

Japanese beetles are pests of gardens. They feed directly on flowers (especially roses) and ruin the aesthetic appearance. Japanese beetle traps consist of a plastic bag with a slow release insecticide. The opening of the bag contains a plastic funnel and lures are placed on the funnel to attract beetles. Most traps use two types of lures, a pheromone lure and a floral attractant lure. Japanese beetle traps kill a lot of beetles, but they only capture part of the population. Additionally, they can attract beetles to the vicinity of the trap. Japanese beetle traps can satisfy the homeowner urge for revenge, but they typically do not adequately protect the plants. For this reason they are not recommended for homeowners.

Flea Control

People who keep cats or dogs as pets commonly have problems with fleas. Fleas can be difficult and expensive to control. Problems with fleas and flea allergies are the most common reason that pet owners visit the veterinarian. There are a number of insecticides that are effective for flea control. Most are applied directly to the skin of the pet and absorbed into the bloodstream. When adult fleas feed on the pet, they receive a lethal dose of the insecticide. Larvae of the cat flea develop off the host and feed on dried blood flakes excreted by the adults. If the pet is treated with an insecticide, the insecticide will be present in the blood flakes and can control larvae in addition to controlling adults.

The insecticide dose needs to be large enough to kill the fleas but small enough to not affect the pet. Flea control products are carefully calibrated. Because cats metabolize and tolerate insecticides less well than dogs, cats should never be given a flea control treatment that is formulated for a dog.

Flea collars are widely marketed as do-it-yourself flea treatments for pet owners. Flea collars can provide some protection to pets. However, the protection declines with distance from the flea collar. The tip of the tail of your pet may be totally unprotected. Pet owners often report poor results with flea collars and end up taking their pet to the vet as the flea problem gets progressively worse.

Flea collars are not for human use. There are reports of their use among troops in Iraq to ward off sand flies and other pests. The flea collars are wrapped around articles of clothing. Flea collars in contact with human skin, especially in extreme heat can cause the flea collar to empty its entire contents in a single day. This can cause skin damage. It is more effective and safer to use combinations of DEET and pyrethroid sprays on the clothing.

Flea Shampoos

Fleas shampoos used to control fleas on pets may contain some soap and fragrance, but they also contain insecticides. People treating their pets with flea shampoo should consider using gloves to minimize their exposure to the insecticide. People treating large numbers of pests in grooming parlors have reported insecticide poisoning symptoms from overexposure to flea shampoo.

Ultrasonic Pest Control Devices

There are numerous devices that produce ultrasound in attempts to discourage pests from entering residences or encouraging the pests to leave. These devices are most commonly marketed for rodent or insect (primarily cockroach) control. These devices do **NOT** work. They are fraudulent. Most insects don't hear ultrasound, and have no reason to avoid the devices. They don't work on mammals, either. This is easily demonstrated by placing a device next to a rodent and observing its non-response. Ultrasonic pest control preys on the desire for pest control measures that affect pests without adverse effects on people and the environment. It is illegal to sell these devices in many states because they violate fraud statutes.

The Indoor Pump Sprayer

The indoor pump sprayer is a device that was developed at Purdue during the 1950s. Prior to this development, there was no good device for applying insecticides indoors. Students in an entomology class at Purdue along with their professor developed a prototype sprayer as a class project. The pump sprayer contains a liquid pesticide formulation. The sprayer can be pressurized and the liquid forced through a spray nozzle.

The sprayer was a big hit with the pest control industry and the students started a company to manufacture and market their sprayer. The B&G sprayer is an industry standard. It was patented and the basis of a multi-million dollar company.

Insecticides

The U.S. Environmental Protection Agency (EPA) definition of an insecticide is "Any agent used to kill or control undesirable insects." The EPA regulates all insecticides whether they kill insects or control them without killing them. For instance, analogs of juvenile hormone that keep mosquito larvae from becoming adults, but don't kill them are considered "insecticides" by EPA.

Insecticides have a wide variety of properties and differ in toxicity, selectivity, and uses. Toxicity varies from highly toxic organophosphorous insecticides (that are restricted to use by professionals only) to insecticides that are so selective, they kill some insects but have no measurable toxicity to people or other non-target organisms. Blanket statements about the safety of all insecticides are not appropriate, because of the diversity of properties.

How Insecticides Work

Insecticides work by disruption of biological processes. Certain chemicals have the ability to interfere with cellular processes and the proper functioning of molecules, especially proteins. The protein targets are often in critical regulatory systems such as the nervous system that controls behavior and movement, cellular respiration that controls energy production, and hormones that control behavior, growth and development. Some insecticides are proteins such as the Bt toxins that can disrupt the function of the insect digestive system.

In order for insecticides to kill an organism, the chemical needs to be delivered to the target site at a high enough concentration. The amount of chemical needed to kill a small animal such as an insect is much less than the amount that is required to kill a large animal. A small amount of an insecticide delivered to a small animal such as an insect will be distributed among the small tissue mass of the insect. If the concentration that reaches the target site is high enough it will kill the insect. The same amount of insecticide in a human would be distributed among a much large tissue mass. The insecticide concentration at the target site would be far more dilute and less likely to be large enough to have an effect. Thus, the primary reason why more insecticide is needed to kill people than insects is because people are larger.

The amount of insecticide needed to kill an organism is proportional to its body weight. An amount of insecticide needed to kill an insect that weighs far less than 1 gram typically has no affect on a 50- to 100-kilogram person. Insecticide toxicity is typically measured on a per weight basis. The units are "mg of insecticides per kg of body weight." Toxicity is usually expressed as LD50, a measure of the dose of insecticide needed to kill half of the test animals in a population. For an insecticide with a toxicity of 100 mg/kg, 0.00001 mg would be needed to kill an average 100-mg insect. A dose of 10,000 mg (about 1 oz) would be needed to kill the average 100-kg person.

Insecticide Detoxification

Our environment is filled with natural toxins, many of them produced by plants to defend themselves against pathogens and herbivores. Animals have evolved in an environment that contains many toxins. Animals have evolved metabolic systems to detoxify and eliminate these toxins. The same metabolic and clearance systems that protect animals from natural plant toxins are effective at metabolizing and clearing (eliminating from the body) synthetically produced chemicals such as insecticides, other pesticides, and drugs.

Differences in detoxification systems among animals can be responsible for differences in toxicity. In general, dogs are much more efficient at metabolizing and eliminating chemicals than cats. The same dose of insecticide that is safe to use on a dog may be harmful to a cat.

Insecticide Selectivity

Insecticides can be far more toxic on a per weight basis to insects than people if there are differences in insecticide target or metabolism. Differential selectivity improves the relative safety of the product to the user. Some chemicals that are not very toxic will be converted to a highly toxic insecticide (activated) in the insect but the same chemical will be metabolized by another route in people without creating the highly toxic insecticide. Chemists have taken advantage of this principle to create a number of "pro-insecticides" that are much safer to humans because of differential metabolism.

Differential selectivity may result if the insecticide disrupts a biological target that is present in insects but absent in people. For example, juvenile hormone analogs are effective for controlling mosquitoes, but have no measurable effect on people because people don't use juvenile hormone. Mosquitoes use juvenile hormone as a signal in their development. Mosquitoes exposed to juvenile hormones remain as larvae and do not develop into biting, disease-transmitting adults. Humans lack receptors that recognize juvenile hormone and suffer no effects.

Another selective insecticide is the Bt protein. Bt is a protein that can be produced in genetically engineered plants. The plants produce Bt that kills insects, but the Bt protein has no effect on people. Bt proteins are currently used in a number of crops (including potatoes and corn) without adverse effects on people. The Bt only kills insects that have a Bt "receptor." Since humans and livestock lack Bt receptors, Bt has little effect on humans or livestock.

Natural Versus Synthetic

Although it is assumed by many people that "natural" insecticides are safer than "synthetic" insecticides, there is no scientific basis for that claim. Most synthetic insecticides are modifications of natural toxins. The modifications can include changes that produce more desirable environmental and safety properties. For instance, new analogs of the insecticide ryanodine are very toxic to insects but have very little toxicity to mammals. In contrast, the natural insecticide, ryanodine, is more toxic to mammals than to insects. This is a clear example that natural insecticides are NOT always safer than synthetic insecticides.

Rules for Insecticide Use

In the United States, the U.S. EPA must approve all insecticides sold. Insecticides are regulated from cradle to grave. Manufacturers are required to test for potential human health and safety hazards and environmental hazards of their products. The EPA reviews all the test data and approves or denies use. There are substantial fines and penalties for submitting incorrect data or failure to fully report known problems.

The EPA approval for use is conditional, subject to a set of rules. These rules are printed on the insecticide container and called "The Label." The label is a legal document that contains all the rules for use and disposal of the product.

Signal Words

The most dangerous pesticides receive the signal word "Danger" on the label, are only available to licensed pesticide applicators and are called "restricted-use pesticides." The EPA has determined that these pesticides require special training or equipment to use safely. Less dangerous pesticides receive the signal word "Warning" and the safest pesticides receive the signal word "Caution." General use pesticides (pesticides available for purchase and use by anyone) most often have the "caution" signal word.

Legal Document

The pesticide label is a legal document. Anyone who uses insecticides is legally bound to follow the rules for use and is liable for any harm that may come from use that is not approved. For safe use of insecticides, always follow instructions, minimize exposure, dispose of properly, keep out of reach of children, and store in original containers. Pesticide containers have instructions printed on the label that are guides to safe and effective use. Using pesticides according to directions protects the user from exposure to harmful doses and protects fish and wildlife. With any insecticide, it is a good idea to use gloves to minimize exposure. It is a good idea to protect skin from exposure (wear long-sleeve clothing and closed shoes—no flip flops) to prevent skin contamination. It is a good idea to wash the skin with soap and water after use to remove unwanted contamination.

Disposal of Unused Insecticides

Many people do not dispose of insecticides properly. In Tippecanoe County, the disposal of pesticides is handled by the Wildcat Creek Waste District at the phone number: 423-2858. DO NOT flush pesticides down toilets, dump them in storm sewers or dump them on the ground. Do mix the pesticide and spray it on foliage to use it completely (according to label) or call the waste disposal program. Only buy as much pesticide as you need to do a job. Disposal is expensive and unlikely to get cheaper. Too many people store hazardous pesticides that are not used. Pesticide containers are typically triple-rinsed and disposed in a landfill. Never use a pesticide container to store other products.

Storage of pesticides can create a hazard for young children. DO NOT store pesticides in unlocked cabinets under the sink where children have easy access. Toddlers often pick up objects and place them in their mouth or will drink from accessible bottles. Pesticides are best stored in a locked cabinet away from children. It is important to keep pesticides in the original container so the pesticide does not become separated from the instructions for use or notes to the physician. Pesticides not in their original containers may be mistaken for food items with tragic consequences.

Pesticide Testing

Pesticides undergo far more safety testing than any other class of chemicals including prescription drugs. This is because pesticides are deliberately placed into the environment. People who do not directly benefit from pesticide use may suffer the costs of unintended effects. Regulation is the best way to protect the public. Wise use requires that we know of the potential hazards in advance so we can guard against their occurrence and quickly remediate problems. Most of the pesticide testing is designed to identify potential hazards. Harm to human health and safety, harm to non-target organisms, residues in food and environmental contamination are all areas of concern. Comprehensive testing is done to determine what could possibly go wrong from use of the pesticides. The testing is done by the companies that produce and market the insecticides. The testing process can take up to 10 years and cost between $10 and $100 million. The high costs of registering a new insecticide means that chemicals are carefully selected for efficacy and safety. Many of the older, less safe, and less environmentally friendly insecticides are being replaced by newer insecticides that are safer to use and cause fewer problems for the environment.

Treatment of Pesticide Poisoning

In spite of steps to protect the public, a small number of people will be victims of pesticide poisoning every year. Treatment of people who have been exposed to pesticides can be summarized in three steps:

1. Remove further contamination
2. Maintain vital signs
3. Have a physician treat symptoms

Contaminated clothing should be removed, especially in the case of a spill, so that additional pesticide exposure does not occur. If the victim is in a building that is contaminated, the victim should be first moved outside. The responder needs to avoid inadvertent pesticide exposure from contact with the victim. Induction of vomiting is controversial. Vomiting can remove an insecticide or other poison that has been ingested. However some pesticides are formulated with solvents that could enter and damage the lungs during vomiting. Except in an emergency, it is best to have a doctor remove the stomach contents through intubation.

"Maintain vital signs" means basic CPR. In severe acute poisoning cases, the most toxic insecticides can cause harm by paralyzing the muscles of the diaphragm. This paralysis prevents air from moving in and out of the lungs. Using CPR to artificially move air in and out of the lungs will maintain oxygen to the brain, keep a victim alive, and prevent brain damage until the poisoning can be treated.

Severe pesticide poisoning requires treatment and care by a physician. The victim needs to be transported to a medical facility. Most physicians will never see a pesticide poisoning and may not be trained in the specifics of the treatment required. The pesticide label contains medical information concerning accidental poisoning including notes to physicians and a 1-800 number telephone hotline. The hotline operates 24/7 and is staffed by individuals trained to give information on pesticide poisoning treatment. The "Notes to Physician" section of the label has information for treatment of symptoms and it is useful to bring the pesticide container to the treating physician. The container identifies the insecticide and the label gives some specific instructions on poisoning treatment. This is important because the appropriate treatment is not the same for all insecticides. Insecticide poisoning is uncommon and most physicians have little experience. The label gives instructions that the physician can use to begin treatment.

Monitoring Pesticide Use

In addition to testing prior to approval of an insecticide, companies are required to monitor and report any health problems of their employees and environmental problems that may arise from use of their products. The EPA reviews these reports and may alter the rules for pesticide use to address unanticipated problems.

For example, fly-by-night pest control companies were purchasing methyl parathion (an insecticide for outdoor use only) and illegally using it indoors in homes, churches, and other structures to control cockroaches. People were getting sick and the treated buildings required expensive decontamination. The people who used the product illegally were fined and jailed, but the problem persisted. EPA threatened to cancel registration of methyl parathion altogether to put a stop to the illegal activity. In order to continue to sell the product for legal uses, the manufacturer had to devise a number of restrictions to prevent illegal use. The manufacturer agreed to: 1) add an odorant to the product so that it would smell bad and prevent its use indoors and 2) only sell the product in containers with a steep deposit, so that unused product would be returned for credit rather than sold at flea markets.

Compliance with Label Specifications

In Indiana, the State Chemist (south end of Biochemistry Building) monitors pesticide quality. Pesticides must meet the standards indicated on the container. Failure to properly meet standards can result in fines.

Pesticides in Food

Consuming small amounts of pesticide in food is not considered harmful. Our bodies have evolved to metabolize and eliminate small quantities of toxins. We ingest many toxins that are contained in plants and our diets. These toxins are metabolized by enzymes in our bodies and eliminated primarily in the urine and feces. The same processes that eliminate plant toxins work to eliminate man-made chemicals including pesticides. Extensive testing is done to determine levels of pesticide in food where no effects are observed. The amount of pesticide allowable in food is usually 100 times lower than the level that produces no effects in test animals. Food is surveyed by the U.S. FDA. Food that exceeds the limits is destroyed. Illegal pesticide residues on food are rare and are preventable if pesticide users properly comply with the directions for use.

Do Pesticides Cause Cancer?

Cancer is one of the largest mortality factors in the United States. Roughly one in every five Americans will die from cancer. It is clear that some environmental contaminants can cause cancer. For example, chemicals in cigarette smoke are carcinogenic. A clear mechanism has been established. The largest increases in cancer deaths in the twentieth century are associated with smoking.

Pesticides are carefully monitored for any association with cancer. Use is discontinued for pesticides that are suspected of a relationship with cancer. Early in the development process, chemicals that are considered for development as pesticides are screened for carcinogenic potential. Chemicals associated with cancer are not pursued for development. In addition, cancer statistics are collected to identify causative agents. Statistical analysis shows that with the exception of lung cancer related to smoking and cancers related to prescription drug use, most cancer mortality is constant or declining, after the introduction of synthetic insecticides in the 1940s and 1950s. This leads us to conclude that pesticides are not causing a noticeable increase in cancer rates.

Pesticide Regulation

Pesticides must be regulated because their use has the potential to cause harm to others. The alternative to regulations are lawsuits. Businesses generally prefer good regulations to lawsuits. Regulations are more predictable, less costly, more fair, and emphasize prevention over more expensive remediation or remuneration. Regulations level the playing field by not allowing irresponsible companies to profit at the expense of responsible companies.

The EPA regulates pesticides according to the following principles:

1. Benefits must outweigh risks
2. Minimize adverse economic impact
3. Health and safety of the public must be protected

Safety Versus Risk

While it is possible to prove that something is NOT safe, safety cannot be guaranteed. Risk can be estimated and risk assessment is fundamental to regulation.
Risk assessment consists of:

> Hazard Identification: Type and extent of harm caused
> Dose Response: How much pesticide is needed to cause harm

Exposure Assessment: How much exposure is associated with use
Risk Characterization: Combines Hazard ID, Dose Response, and Exposure

Hazard identification involves a comprehensive suite of tests designed to detect potential harm to human health, non-target organisms, and environmental contamination. Over 140 tests may be required. It is important to know what can go wrong. When something does go wrong, there will be no delay in taking the appropriate actions. Most pesticide testing is done to identify hazards and determine the dose of insecticide required to cause harm.

Risk characterization sets exposure goals that will protect the public and environment. Risk characterization is based on first understanding the potential hazards, and then measuring the amount of the pesticide necessary to cause harm (dose response). For any chemical, there is a concentration that is low enough to be not harmful. Establishing the minimum dose that causes harm is important for regulation. The No Observable Adverse Effect Level (NOAEL) is the maximum pesticide dose that has no harmful effect.

Pesticides are managed so that the exposure is kept below the NOAEL divided by a safety factor, typically, 100. This is to provide an extra margin of safety. For example, if no effect from a pesticide was seen below 1 mg/kg, then the pesticide would be regulated so that exposure was held to under 0.01 mg/kg.

Risk Management

The tools and rules for managing exposure to insecticides are used in the process of risk management. Risk management considers science, economic, social, and legal issues. Rules are continuously evaluated, reviewed, and revised. Risk management requires value judgments. For instance, harm to wildlife or endangered species is difficult to assign a monetary value. Some people value these species more than others. The value each individual would assign is "subjective." In the regulation process, regulators must develop a consensus that is acceptable to the majority.

The outcome of the risk management process is the set of instructions on the pesticide label that if followed, will protect human health and safety and the environment. The rules are proposed by the manufacturer and must be approved by the EPA. There is flexibility in determining which measures are most effective and appropriate. If rules are too restrictive and do not make sense to the user, compliance will be poor. The manufacturer can in some cases modify the formulation of the product and product packaging to improve safety. If the product as formulated is a hazard, then applicators may be required to wear personal protective equipment (gloves, breathing air filters, etc). Other tools include engineering controls, use restrictions, applicator training, notifications, re-entry intervals, and cancellation.

All pesticide applications require a re-entry interval. Often pesticides are applied as liquids that are readily transferred to the skin of unprotected people and animals. Once the liquid dries, the chemical does not transfer as efficiently to the skin of people who enter the area. The minimum re-entry period after an insecticide application is always "until the application is dry." For some highly toxic pesticides used in special applications, a re-entry interval can be longer than a week. Lawn care companies that treat with pesticides will place warning flags in treated areas. It is best practice to avoid treated areas until the re-entry period has elapsed.

EPA approval is always conditional and subject to review. Companies are legally obligated to report problems with their product to the EPA. These problems are reviewed. When concerns arise, the rules for use must be changed or in some cases, all uses of the product will be eliminated. The EPA will further monitor to determine if the new set of rules solves the problem. If not, the product review will continue and a new set of rules (or product elimination) must be considered.

Conclusion

Insect control is important to our health and safety, but some insect control agents are capable of causing harm. The insecticide DDT demonstrates the positives and negatives. DDT was used extensively in WWII to control insect borne diseases. DDT prevented millions of cases of malaria and severe outbreaks of typhus. A Nobel Prize was awarded for establishing the importance of DDT for controlling insect pests.

However, a few decades later, use of DDT was banned because of problems with environmental contamination. DDT was applied in large quantities to the environment and its residues were too persistent. DDT was transported globally and accumulated in the tissues of animals (including people). DDT even appeared in the tissues of animals in the arctic, far from its original sites of application.

Important lessons have been learned from the mistakes made with DDT and other pesticides. This has led to extensive testing of new pesticides before they are used and the replacement of the old pesticides that have a high risk to health, safety, or environment with newer chemicals that pose far lower health, safety, and environmental risks. There is no silver bullet to insect pest control. Each method will have its own set of potentially negative side effects. The regulatory process is necessary to minimize the risks to the environment while protecting the health and safety of the public.

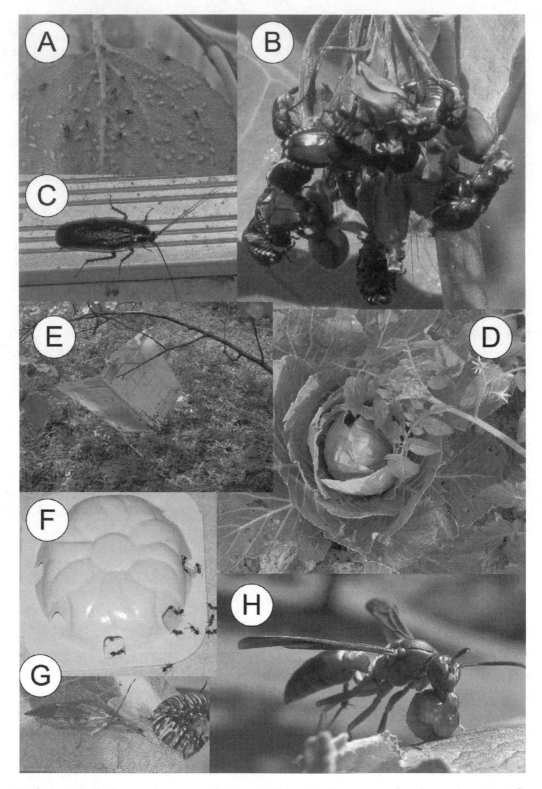

A. Soybean aphids reduce soybean yields B. Japanese beetles destroy flower gardens   C. Cockroaches are pests that can cause asthma   D. Cabbage worms eat holes in the leaves and destroy cabbage   E. Yellow sticky card for monitoring insects   F. Ant bait station for ant control   G. Stink bugs are important biological control agents   H. Wasps are important biological control agents.

Chapter 11 Study Guide

1. Define economic injury level.

2. How are degree days used in pest management?

3. How arc insect traps used in IPM?

4. What is cultural control? Give three examples.

5. What is biological control? Give an example.

6. How is crop rotation used to control insects?

7. What gene is commonly used to make plants resistant to insects?

8. Of ant bait stations, bug zappers, and Japanese beetle traps, which ones effectively solve the insect problem?

9. Why are bug zappers not permitted in food establishments?

10. What precaution should you use with flea shampoos? Why?

11. Define insecticide. Would a pheromone be an insecticide?

12. What are two ways of achieving differential selectivity of insecticides? Give an example of each.

13. What information is included on a pesticide label?

14. What are the steps to be taken in case of a pesticide poisoning?

15. Define hazard identification.

16. How is risk assessment used in pesticide regulation?

17. How is risk management used?

18. What insecticide is associated with the Nobel Prize?

19. Are natural insecticides safer than synthetic insecticides?

20. Is pesticide exposure a major cause of cancer?

Chapter 12

Insects and Crime

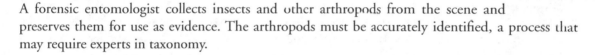

Forensic entomology is the use of insects and other arthropods as evidence in legal matters. Insects are ubiquitous in our environment, so it is not surprising to find insects at the scene of a crime or at the center of a civil suit. Three primary areas of application for forensic entomology are: 1) food contamination (stored product) cases, 2) urban pest control cases (primarily structural damage by termites and termite control), and 3) medico-legal applications that include but are not limited to investigations of deaths (murder, suicide, accidental), assaults, rapes, physical abuse, and neglect.

A forensic entomologist collects insects and other arthropods from the scene and preserves them for use as evidence. The arthropods must be accurately identified, a process that may require experts in taxonomy.

Forensic entomologists must be experts in the biology of the insects they collect as evidence. Forensic entomologists conduct numerous studies to determine biological facts that are necessary to make conclusions about the accuracy of testimony. Some of the most important biological characteristics are the species distribution (both geographical and ecological) and the phenology of the insect (when and what life stages are commonly found). These characteristics can be used to establish probable times and locations of the events.

Food Contamination Cases

For example, a witness claims that an insect contaminant was present in a can of food. Is the insect evidence consistent with the species and life stages present in the area where the food was harvested, processed, or stored during those times? If the insect is a species and life stage that is common in those locations, then the evidence is consistent with contamination occurring during processing. If the species or life stage is not found in the area during the critical time interval, then that evidence would cast doubt that the contamination occurred during processing and cast suspicion on product tampering by the plaintiff. In this example, interpretation of the evidence requires knowledge about the phenology, development, habitats, and distribution of the insect species.

Urban Cases

Structural damage from insect pests such as termites can lead to litigation between property owners and pest control companies. Forensic entomologists may be called as witnesses to testify about the insect damage evidence and best practices for pest control.

Murder Cases

Studies of the patterns of insect arrival and colonization (ecological succession) and rates of insect development are important for interpreting insect evidence collected from dead bodies. Insect evidence can be used to establish the post-mortem interval (PMI) or the time expired between death and discovery of a dead body.

Stages of Decomposition

Decomposition of dead animals can be divided into several stages (Fresh, Bloat, Decay, and Dry) based on the physical condition of the remains. Immediately after death, a body in the fresh stage will start to decompose due to the action of microorganisms on the tissues. This process will release odors that are attractive to insects, especially blow flies. Microorganisms degrade proteins and alter the body tissues in ways that make them more amenable to feeding by insects. Microorganisms release internal gasses that cause the corpse to swell or "bloat." The swelling marks the end of the fresh stage and beginning of the bloat stage. As decomposition progresses, the body cavity will become compromised and the gasses escape, marking the end of the bloat stage. The bloat stage is following by the decay stage when the action of microorganisms on the tissues renders them even more suitable for insect feeding. During the decay stage, most of the remains are consumed by insects and microorganisms. Eventually, the remains will become dry. During the dry stage, insects that feed on cartilage, hair and other remaining tissue will colonize.

Insect Colonization Of Dead Bodies

Insects found on dead bodies may be grouped according to their ecological guilds including necrophages, omnivores, predators, and parasitoids and incidentals. The necrophages feed on the tissue of the dead body directly. They are often the first insects to colonize the body. Flies and beetles are among the most important necrophages. Insects, such as blow flies, that lay eggs on recently dead bodies have olfactory systems that can detect the odor of death at a substantial distance shortly after the death has occurred. These early colonizing insects are typically good fliers and their success depends on being one of the first to arrive at the site.

The omnivores feed on both the dead body tissues and are predators of insects (especially fly larvae) that are feeding on the remains. The omnivores typically arrive later than the necrophages. Predators and parasitoids of the necrophages will arrive and colonize only after the necrophages are established. Omnivores, predators, and parasitoids can slow the rate of decomposition by reducing the number of necrophages. Incidentals are primarily soil dwelling arthropods (pill bugs, centipedes, mites, and insects) that are located in close proximity to the remains.

Forensic entomologists study patterns of insect colonization of dead bodies (both animal and human) in numerous habitats and geographical locations. The species that are found are identified and the relative numbers, time of arrival, and condition of the remains during the times the insects are present are all noted. The most important species for medico-legal investigations are flies and beetles. Blow flies are common necrophages that are often the first to colonize the remains and are therefore the most important for determining PMI. Beetles such as rove beetles, hister beetles, and carrion beetles are all attracted to dead animals. The carrion beetles consume the remains directly. The rove and hister beetles are predators or omnivores that feed on fly maggots. These species may also contribute to the determination of PMI.

Blow Flies and PMI

When temperatures and environmental conditions are suitable for activity, blow flies are typically the first insects to arrive on a corpse and are responsible for much of the decomposition. If blow flies are active, they will typically arrive at a corpse within 1 hour of death during daylight hours. The predominant species of blow fly may change according to season and geographical location.

Blow fly larvae have difficulty penetrating intact adult skin. Female blow flies concentrate their egg laying on exposed openings such as the mouth, nose, and eyes. Eggs hatch after 8 to 24 hours and the larvae begin feeding on internal tissues. The requirement for blowflies to use body openings for colonization determines a pattern of decomposition. Those areas of the body nearest the openings will be consumed first. Trauma that creates an open wound can alter the pattern of decomposition by allowing blow flies to initially colonize parts of the body that are distant from natural openings.

Blow flies have three larval stages that can be distinguished by size and appearance. Mature larvae will leave the corpse en masse and burrow into the nearby soil to pupate. Depending on the temperature, pupae continue to develop into adults or pause development and enter an overwintering stage. All life stages, eggs, larvae, pupae, and adults can be important evidence.

To accurately estimate the PMI, the forensic entomologist must know the rate of development of the insect species found on the dead body. However, the rate of insect development is dependent on environmental conditions, especially temperature. Therefore, forensic entomologists must conduct studies under different environmental conditions on each important species.

Numerous studies show that most insects have a "base temperature" or temperature below which no growth occurs. As the temperature increases above the base temperature, growth is more rapid up to an optimum temperature. The relationship between growth and temperature is often described by the temperature measures, accumulated degree days (ADD) or accumulated degree hours. A single degree day is calculated as the average temperature for the day minus the base temperature (The base temperature is the lower threshold for blowfly development). The values for each day are summed to calculate the ADD. For example, if the base temperature is 10 degrees centigrade and the average temperature for Monday, Tuesday, and Wednesday are 15, 20, and 18, respectively, then the degree days (average minus base temperature) would be 5, 10, and 8 degree days, respectively. The ADD for the period Monday through Wednesday would be 5 + 10 + 8 (the sum of the degree days) or 23 degree days.

For each species of interest, forensic entomologists conduct controlled laboratory studies of development at different temperatures. The mode of the ADD (the most frequent number of ADD) required for the insect to reach each developmental stage and size are calculated. From these experiments, forensic entomologists determine the number of degree days required by an insect to go from egg to each of the developmental stages that might be found on a dead body.

Forensic entomologists use the degree day model to estimate the PMI. The insects in the most advanced developmental stage are identified to species. The ADD required for the insects to reach that developmental stage are available from previous studies. The ADD is related to the length of time the body has been dead. To convert ADD to time, the forensic entomologist must retrieve weather data from a nearby weather station. Working backward in time from the date of the insect evidence collection, the forensic entomologist calculates the degree days for each previous day (average minus base temperature). The minimum number of degree days that must be summed to reach an ADD meets or exceeds the ADD required for insect to reach the stage collected from the body is the minimum time the body has been dead. In this way, the date of death is estimated.

Other Insects and PMI

In Indiana, blow flies are one of the most important insects for estimating PMI of bodies that are in the early stages of decomposition. The presence of other insect species can become more important if the time of death is several months or if the death occurred when it is too cold for blow flies to be active (such as winter). Some of the beetle species (such as rove and carrion beetles) prey on fly larvae and arrive later. Other species of insects arrive only after the body has been mostly consumed by blow flies and other early arrivals.

Geographic location

Evidence used by forensic entomologists is not restricted to colonizers of dead bodies. Insects and small arthropods are common in the environment and may become attached to people or evidence. Chiggers (a type of mite) and ticks can attach to people involved in a crime. Because these have limited distributions, they can be used to link a suspect to a site or area. Small arthropods may also become attached to the victims and be transported with the victim. This can indicate that the body was moved after death. Insects may become attached to items used during a crime. For example, automobiles often collide with flying insects. Dead insects can be collected from radiators and grills to be used as evidence linking an automobile (and by extension, a person) to a location.

Insects that are only present in aquatic environments can tie evidence to aquatic locations. Similarly, insects that are only present in wooded areas, open fields, meadows, deserts or mountains can be used to establish location. The ability to use insects as evidence requires a body of knowledge about insect natural history and ecology.

Toxicological Evidence from Insects

When insects consume body tissue, the insect will also consume drugs or other toxins that are present in the tissue. Even if the body is too decomposed for toxin or drug analysis, it may be possible to conduct an analysis on the insect to indicate the presence of toxins.

Some toxins are known to alter the rate of growth. Many toxins will be toxic to the insects and inhibit the rate of growth. However, some toxins, such as cocaine may stimulate growth of some insects such as blow fly larvae.

Insects in Cases of Abuse and Neglect

Unsanitary conditions can attract insect colonization. Flies such as house flies and filth flies are attracted to human waste and will lay eggs on that waste. In cases of abuse and neglect, victims may be allowed to lie in their own waste for extended periods. The presence of fly larvae in waste material can be used as physical evidence that the victim was not receiving proper and timely care.

DNA Evidence

DNA is important evidence for establishing the identities of people involved in a crime. Insects that come in contact with people or feed on people can be important sources of DNA evidence. It is possible to recover human DNA from insects and use that DNA in marker studies that help establish identity.

Maggot Therapy

In addition to their use in forensic investigations, blow fly larvae have a medical use in wound therapy. Blow fly larvae will consume only necrotic and decomposing tissue and do not feed on healthy tissue. Blow flies secrete antibiotics into the wound that can inhibit the growth of undesirable microorganisms and stimulate wound healing. Maggot therapy can work on wounds that are in the initial stages of gangrene. Thus, blow flies can be used to treat wounds that are otherwise difficult or impossible to treat. One important use for maggot therapy is the treatment of wounds in diabetics. In some cases, these wounds do not respond to any other treatment and the patient is faced with amputation of a limb as a life saving measure. Some wounds that are untreatable other than through amputation have responded successfully to maggot therapy.

How it works. Sterile blow fly larvae are marketed for treating wounds. Live maggots are placed directly on the wound and confined by a container and dressing that restricts their movement to the wound site. After an appropriate feeding interval (typically 24–48 hours), the maggots are removed and the wound rinsed, treated, and dressed according to standard practice. Maggot therapy is not painful, does not cause discomfort, and is much preferable to drastic amputations.

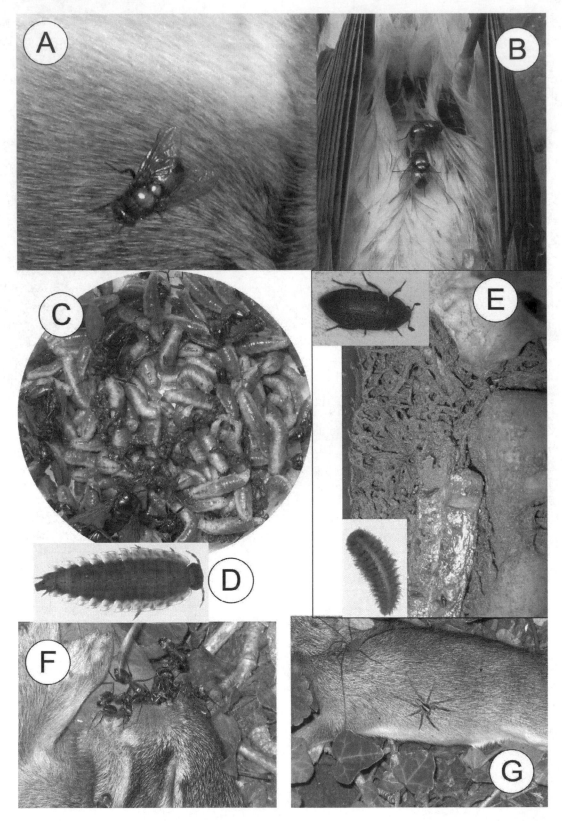

A. Blow flies are often the first insect to arrive at a dead animal.   B. Blow flies laying eggs on dead bird.   C. Blow fly maggots.   D. Silphid beetle larva.   E. Dermestid beetles feed on dry remains. Insets: Top- Adult. Bottom- Larva.   F. Ants feed on dead animal near their nest.   G. Spiders await prey attracted to a dead animal.

Chapter 12 Study Questions

1. Define forensic entomology.

2. What is the post-mortem interval?

3. What is the most important insect in establishing the post-mortem interval?

4. How are degree days used in calculating post-mortem interval?

5. How can insects provide information about the location of a crime?

6. What properties of maggots make them so useful for maggot therapy?

Chapter 13

Insect Nutrition

Why Are the Nutritional Needs of All Living Organisms Similar?

The nutritional needs of an organism are the sum of the needs of its cells and the secretions of those cells. All cells are related through descent with modification from the ancestral cells that evolved billions of years ago. All cells share the same basic structures and many of the same genes. This is true for bacterial cells, plant cells, insect cells, and even human cells. Although there are some differences in the ratios of the components, the basic building blocks of all cells are the same.

To understand the nutritional needs of an organism, it is useful to start with the needs of its cells. All living cells have the same basic components including:

Water
Lipids/sterols
Proteins
Carbohydrates
Nucleic acids
Vitamins
Minerals

What role do these materials have in a cell?

Water

Water is an essential nutrient. The inside of the cell is filled with water. The components of the cell are "dissolved or suspended in water." Water facilitates the diffusion and transport of molecules within the cell and is important in many biochemical reactions. Cells will not function properly if they lack sufficient water. Without sufficient water, too many of the important cells will die and eventually lead to the death of the organism.

Multi-cellular organisms typically contain extracellular water. The extracellular water is used as a fluid for transport of nutrients to the cells and waste products away from the cells. Extracellular fluid may be used for movement or maintaining body structure through the hydraulic properties of water.

Lipids/Sterols

Lipids and sterols have an important structural role in the cell as well as being a source of stored energy within a cell. The contents of all cells are contained within a membrane. The membrane is made of lipids and sterols. The membrane prevents the biological molecules within the cell from floating away and prevents unwanted external molecules from entering the cell.

Multi-cellular animals may also secrete lipids in form of waxes, oils, and grease. The exoskeleton of insects is coated with a waterproof layer of lipids. Among the insects a wide variety of lipids are secreted including commercial products such as bees wax.

Proteins

Proteins are the most diverse molecules in a cell. Proteins are long chains (polymers) made from smaller units (amino acids). There are twenty amino acids found in proteins. The properties of the protein are determined by the kind and order of the amino acids in a protein chain. Biologically important amino acid chains can range in length from a few amino acids to several hundred. The variety of proteins that can be produced by different combinations of the twenty amino acids is enormous. The instructions to make all the proteins a cell needs are stored in DNA as genes.

Proteins are involved in every function of the cell. All cells have an internal skeleton made of proteins. This internal structure gives shape to the cells, is responsible for cell movements and for transport of molecules within the cell. Some proteins are imbedded in the lipid membrane and help regulate the transport of molecules in and out of the cells. Some proteins are "enzymes" that are responsible for processing nutrients and synthesizing the cell components.

Carbohydrates

Carbohydrates (sugars and starches) are energy storage molecules in most animals. Animal cells can "burn" sugars to produce energy. The process of sugars reacting with oxygen is tightly controlled to capture most of the energy available in the sugar. The waste products from "burning" sugar are carbon dioxide and water. This process is similar in all cells.

Chitin is a carbohydrate that insects and other arthropods use as a component of their exoskeleton. Chitin is both strong and flexible. Chitin can be obtained in quantities large enough for commercial use from shell fish. Commercial applications of chitin include the production of bandages that are superior to traditional cotton bandages in halting bleeding from wounds and antibacterial properties.

Nucleic Acids

Nucleic acids are long chains (polymers) of smaller molecules (nucleotides). DNA is the nucleic acid that stores all the information (genes) for making proteins needed to run the cell. The nucleic acid RNA has a primary role in the control and synthesis of proteins. The nucleotides are used as building blocks for molecules involved in energy transfer reactions and as hormones in many cells.

Vitamins

Vitamins are biomolecules that do not fit in any of the above categories. Vitamins have important functions in cellular processes. Some cells have lost the capability to make their own vitamins. These molecules must then be obtained by feeding on other organisms. Insects may harbor microorganisms that produce and secrete vitamins. These microorganisms have access to food ingested by insects, are protected from the environment and are transferred from insect to insect. The insects gain a source of vitamins.

Minerals

Minerals are inorganic molecules (such as phosphate, sodium, potassium, chlorine, etc.). Minerals are important for communication within a cell and may be necessary for some cell processes. Minerals are especially important in signaling by the nervous system and movements of the muscles.

Acquiring Nutrients

All cells utilize common minerals and water, "inorganic materials" that are widely available on earth. Minerals and water may be taken from both living and non-living sources. Photosynthetic cells are capable of using the energy from sunlight, to turn water, carbon dioxide and minerals into proteins, carbohydrates, lipids, sterols, and nucleic acids.

Most living organisms that lack photosynthesis (including all insects) must acquire proteins, carbohydrates, lipids, sterols, and nucleic acids from other organisms. The ultimate source for most of these biological molecules is green plants.

Some insects obtain these biological molecules directly from plants. Insects that feed directly on plants are called "herbivores." Other insects feed on animals or animal products. Insects that entirely consume other living animals are called "predators". An example of an insect predator is the praying mantis. This insect captures and eats many insects in its lifetime. Insects that live on a host animal without killing it are called "parasites." Lice are insects that are parasites of humans. Fleas are parasites of many animals including our pet dogs and cats. Some insects grow and develop inside other insects and are called "parasitoids." Parasitoids will be discussed in more detail later in the course.

Some insects feed on dead plants and animals. These insects are called "scavengers" and have a unique and important role in our ecosystem. Larvae of flies and some beetles eat the flesh of dead animals or consume the manure. Without insects to remove the dead carcasses or waste products from our environment, we would be literally knee-deep in "undesirable waste products."

Adaptation to Foods

Each insect species is adapted to its own nutritional source(s). Some insects are capable of completing their entire life cycle within the seed of a plant. Other insects need a variety of food sources to develop and reproduce. The ability of insects to specialize on food sources has promoted the evolution of a large number and diversity of insect species.

While all organisms share the same basic building blocks, some organisms may produce toxic chemicals that prevent other organisms from eating them. Many of the green plants produce toxins that can make animals sick or even kill them. Only insects that have developed a capacity to neutralize the toxins are able to use those toxic plants as a food source.

Usually the nutritional needs of the insect do not exactly match the nutrition available in the food. Insects can compensate in several ways including overeating and getting nutrition from multiple sources. Aphids are insects that massively overeat. Aphids feed on plant sap that is very high in sugars but very low in other nutrients. Aphids consume large amounts of sap and excrete copious amounts of water and sugars in order to get enough of the proteins and other nutrients they need.

Some insects have symbiotic microorganisms that live in their guts or in special structures inside the insect. These microorganisms supply some of the biomolecules that the insects cannot make for themselves. For example, termites contain microorganisms that rapidly digest cellulose. The microorganisms are supplied with a steady supply of cellulose from the termites feeding on wood. The microorganisms have a suitable, sheltered place to live inside the termites. The termites get help digesting the wood from their microorganisms and are supplied with additional biomolecules they need to develop and reproduce more rapidly.

Many insects will feed on multiple sources in order to get a better mix of nutrients. Plant leaves are often high in carbohydrates but too low in proteins. Pollen is very high in protein but low in carbohydrates. Some insects will feed on both pollen and leaves to get a better ratio of protein to carbohydrate in their diet.

Diet Self-Selection

Some insects have the ability to regulate the ratios of protein and carbohydrate in their diet. The corn earworm (a caterpillar that feeds on ears of corn) eats both the corn silk (high in protein) and the kernels (high in carbohydrate). When given a choice of artificial diets containing protein (and no carbohydrate) or carbohydrate (and no protein), the caterpillar will wander back and forth between the two diets. About 80 percent of what the caterpillar eats will come from the protein diet and 20 percent from the carbohydrate diet. The caterpillar has an internal mechanism that tells it to seek another type of food. Caterpillars, like humans get "cravings" for certain types of foods. If a caterpillar gets too much sugar, it will "crave" a food with higher protein. If the food does not have enough sugar, the caterpillar will "crave" a food with more sugar.

Artificial Diets

An artificial diet is specially prepared food that substitutes for the natural diet of an insect. Artificial diets are useful for keeping insects for laboratory experiments. For example, to keep a caterpillar (such as a tomato hornworm) all year round would require leaves from a lot of tomato plants. In temperate areas, tomato plants do not survive outdoors in the winter. It is usually easier to buy commercial ingredients and raise the caterpillars on an artificial diet. Unfortunately, not all insects can thrive on an artificial diet.

An insect that thrives on artificial diet is the caterpillar of the tomato hornworm. The artificial diet described below contains all the nutrients the caterpillar needs to grow and develop into an adult. This diet is similar to many artificial insect diets.

Agar. The basic artificial diet is created using agar, a carbohydrate that dissolves when heated in water and cools to a gelatinous material. The cooled agar contains a matrix of internal spaces. Materials blended into the heated agar will be contained in the internal spaces when the agar cools. The liquid diet can be poured into a tray and will solidify. The agar can be cut into appropriate sized blocks.

Water. All the water that the caterpillar needs is contained within the agar matrix of the diet. In nature, caterpillars get all their water from eating leaves and do not need to "drink" free water.

Cellulose is a (mostly non-digestible) carbohydrate added to the diet to provide bulk.

Sugar (sucrose) is added as a source of energy and building block for more complex carbohydrates (such as chitin).

Protein. The protein sources for the caterpillar are casein (milk protein) and wheat germ, which contains both proteins and lipids/sterols.

Lipids. Corn oil is added as an additional source of lipids and sterol. Cholesterol is added to boost sterol content. Insects are capable of metabolizing plant sterols and cholesterol into a range of sterols important to insect biology.

Minerals and vitamins. A mixture of the important minerals (Wesson's salts) and vitamins are added. Many of the vitamins added to insect diet are the same ones that are common components of vitamin supplements for humans.

Preservatives. The resulting diet would be a great source of food for many microorganisms. Some of the components would rapidly go rancid (oxidize) without preservatives. Antibiotics are added to prevent the growth of microorganisms and antioxidants are added to prevent the food from becoming rancid.

The artificial diet will "keep" at room temperature for over a week and can be stored refrigerated for several weeks. The artificial diet must maintain its quality under temperatures suitable for insect growth and development. Ideally, the diet quality remains good throughout the feeding period of the insect. If not, the diet would need to be replaced periodically.

Wheat germ:
Protein, sterols

Sugar:
Energy, Chitin

Casein:
Protein

Vitamins:
Cell Processes

Artificial
Diet

Agar:
Diet Matrix

Corn oil:
Lipids
Cell Membranes
Epicuticle

Cellulose:
Fiber

Minerals:
Cell Processes

Antioxidant

Antibiotic

Artificial diet contains all the nutrients (including water) that a caterpillar needs to grow and develop. Cells of all living organisms are related by descent with modification and require the same common nutrients for reproduction, growth and maintenance.

Chapter 13 Study Questions

1. What is the role of the following nutrients in cells?
    a. Lipids

    b. Proteins

    c. Carbohydrates

    d. Nucleic acids

    e. Minerals

f. Vitamins

g. Water

2. How may insects adapt to a mismatch between the nutritional composition of their diet and their own nutritional composition?

3. What is the role of antibiotics in artificial diet?

4. What is the role of antioxidants in artificial diet?

Chapter 14

Rearing Insects for Science and Profit

Why Rear Insects?

There are several reasons for rearing insects. These include for profit (from insect products or the insects themselves), for food, for purposes of scientific study, and for pleasure.

Insect for Profit

Honey Bees

The number one insect reared for profit is the honey bee. Bees are reared for the products, (honey and beeswax) as well as for their value as pollinators. Many of our food crops are insect pollinated. A crop that is well pollinated will produce more fruit than a crop that is poorly pollinated. Farmers may pay beekeepers to set up hives in their orchards or fields. Domesticated honey bee colonies live in special hive boxes built by beekeepers. The colonies must be checked for diseases and parasites and treated if necessary. The amounts of honey are managed and enough stores must be maintained to allow the colony to survive the winter. More information on bee biology and beekeeping are in the chapter on honey bees.

Predators and Parasitoids

One method of controlling insects that damage valuable plants is to release insect predators and parasitoids. When successful, the predators and parasitoids will eat and kill enough of the pests to keep damage to plants at a minimum. In some cases (especially in glasshouses) these biological control agents can be more effective than pesticides. There are companies that specialize in rearing predatory insects (such as mantids) and parasitoid insects. The rearing method differs depending on the insect. Often parasitoid rearing requires maintaining large colonies of the host insect. The parasitoids that are sold are collected from the parasitized hosts.

Meal Worms

Meal worms are the larvae of beetles. Meal worms make good fish bait and pet food (birds, lizards, snakes, and fish). They are commonly available in bait shops or pet stores. Mealworms can be pests of stored products and are easy to rear. Mealworms will feed on oatmeal, whole wheat or other grains. They can be reared in a small jar with a screen at room temperature. It can be useful to give them a small piece of apple or potato as a moisture source.

Some pet owners raise mealworms on a nutrient rich diet prior to feeding them to their pet (a practice known as gut loading). The pet gets nutrients present in the mealworm gut in addition to the nutrients in the mealworm itself.

Butterflies

Butterflies are fragile and their wings are easily damaged. To obtain undamaged specimens, many butterfly collectors will rear adults from the caterpillars. The caterpillars are kept in a container and fed leaves of their native host plants. The caterpillars will form a pupa and emerge into an undamaged adult butterfly. Some butterflies such as the Morpho are very difficult to collect because they fly and roost among the tree tops. There is a substantial trade in Morpho butterflies. Most of the traded specimens are produced from caterpillars.

Butterfly collectors have produced extensive records of suitable caterpillar host plants in their attempts to produce specimens for collections. This information is valuable to scientists who study insect diets. Because of butterfly collectors, we know more about the diets of butterflies than any other group of insects.

Insects for Scientific Research

Scientists need living insects to study behavior, physiology, ecology, and genetics. Numerous insects have been successfully reared in laboratories around the world. Insect rearing can be time consuming and expensive. One might wonder, "Why can insects that produce massive numbers and become pests in the wild be so difficult to maintain in a laboratory?" The short answer is that the conditions in the wild are not always easily reproduced in the laboratory. Insects may require a specific type of plant as food and not thrive on an artificial diet. Insects may suffer from diseases when confined in a laboratory. Insects may have special requirements for temperature and humidity. Insects may fail to reproduce in captivity. An extensive scientific literature on caring for insects in culture has been developed.

Fruit Flies

T.H. Morgan pioneered the use of the fruit fly, Drosophila, in genetic research. Morgan needed an organism that had variable genetic traits and reproduced quickly. The fruit fly life cycle is about 2 weeks, making it ideal for genetic experiments that require many generations. Fruit flies can produce twenty-six generations per year. This allows geneticists to breed fruit flies twenty-six times faster than animals that have only one generation per year. Fruit flies are easily reared on an artificial diet in a small tube. Millions of fruit flies will fit in a small room. The cost of rearing fruit flies is low compared to other animals.

Fruit flies can be exposed to radiation to induce mutations. Fruit flies have a "polytene" chromosome in their salivary glands that made it possible to visualize fruit fly chromosome and make a map of the gene location. Drosophila was one of the first animals with a completely sequenced genome. A lot of effort has developed Drosophila into a potent research tool. Because all organisms are related by descent with modification, most Drosophila genes have homologues (similar genes) in humans. What we learn about Drosophila genes can help us understand human genes and enhance our efforts to cure genetic diseases.

Dermestid Beetles

Many museums that display skeletons of animals keep a colony of Dermestid beetles. The Dermestids are scavengers that eat the flesh off the bone but do not damage the bones. If given no other source of food, these ravenous beetles will completely pick the bones clean, saving the curators hours of tedious work. Dermestid beetles "rear themselves." They only require a source of water and an occasional piece of meat from the butcher.

Rearing Insects as a Hobby

Ants

Well over 1 million ant farms have been sold in the United States. Ant farms are popular with people that like to spend time watching others work. The typical ant farm consists of two vertical panes of glass separated by a short distance. The space between the glass plates is filled with sand or in some ant farms a nutritive gel. Ants are added (best if a queen is present) and the ants will make their tunnels and rear their young in plain view. The ants need a source of water and food that is appropriate for the ant species.

Other Pets

Some types of beetles (especially stag beetles) are reared as pets. In some countries such as Japan, a stag beetle may fetch several thousand dollars. There are very detailed manuals for how to rear stag beetles. Most of stag beetles require a very moist environment. Some of them are difficult to rear, thus the high price.

Madagascar (hissing) cockroaches are popular "pets" and are sold in pet stores. These insects are scavengers and will eat a wide variety of food. They need a source of water.

Insect Feeding Considerations

Not all insects will eat all foods. This is especially true of herbivorous insects. It is important to match the plant to the insect. A species of insect that eats tomato leaves may not eat grass. Plants vary in nutritional quality and may not be suitable if damaged or stressed (even if they are the correct species). Some plants may be treated with pesticides that are harmful to insects. Produce that is organically grown (not treated with pesticide) is preferable for insect food.

Predators and parasitoids need to be matched with appropriate prey or hosts. Small mantids thrive best on small prey such as fruit flies. As mantids increase in size, they require increasingly larger prey items. Many parasitoids will only develop on one or a few host species. Like herbivores, it is important to match your insect with a suitable host.

Artificial diet is the easiest and most consistent food source for an insect if a diet is available. Artificial diets must provide the insect with all the nutrients necessary for growth and reproduction. The nutrients must be present in acceptable ratios. Some insects require very special chemicals to initiate feeding. Not only must the artificial diet satisfy the physiological requirements of the insect, it must trigger insect behaviors to eat and consume the diet in sufficient quantities. If the proper behavioral cues are not present, an insect may starve or dehydrate even though a source of food and water is available.

Humidity/Water

Insects fail to thrive if conditions are too moist or too dry. Humidity can be increased by providing water to evaporate. Humidity can be decreased by moving dry air through the container. Some insects are adapted to life in very dry environments and need little added moisture to survive. Many plant-feeding insects do not drink and obtain all their water requirements from the plants they eat. Some insects do drink and require a source of free water. Free water can contribute to growth of molds. Water is typically confined to vials with cotton wicks or small watering dishes. These are designed to provide access to water but minimize mold.

Temperature

Temperature has a large influence on insect development. Extreme heat or cold can kill insects. Insects typically develop most rapidly and thrive within an optimal temperature range. Insects will develop more slowly and suffer greater mortality at temperatures warmer or cooler than the optimal.

Sanitation/Allergies

Some people develop allergies to insects, especially after long periods of exposure. Scales of moths or external and internal insect proteins can cause allergic reactions in some people. People who rear large numbers of insects must be concerned with limiting their exposure. Allergy is not common in people with limited exposure to only one or a few insects.

Pests/Diseases

Insects in a colony can be attacked by pests or contract diseases. Laboratory colonies may be attacked by nematodes, ants, and other pests. Honey bees commonly have mite infestations that must be treated. Mites can destroy bee colonies if infestations are large.

Insects are susceptible to diseases caused by viruses, bacteria, fungi, and other microorganisms. Insects have diseases and get sick the same way other pets and even people do. Sanitation and keeping cages clean is important for reducing diseases. Most insect-rearing protocols include sanitation measures to prevent diseases from entering the colony.

Photoperiod/Diapause

Some insects will enter a dormant phase (diapause) to live through environmentally unfavorable conditions such as a cold winter. In nature, diapause is often triggered by the reduction in day length as time passes from summer to winter. For example, in June in Indiana it is daylight for over 15 hours and dark for less than 9 hours (a 15:9 photoperiod). On the first day of autumn, there are 12 hours of light and 12 hours of darkness. Insects may respond to photoperiod by entering a resting phase called diapause. Insects in diapause have a lower metabolism, are inactive and development is nearly or completely halted. To prevent insects in colony from entering diapause, the insects are kept under a light cycle of at least 15 hours of light.

Your Insect Pets

Keeping an insect as a pet and taking daily notes on its behavior and development is a great way to learn more about insects. Some insects are very easy to rear and make good classroom activities. Two of the easiest insects to rear are the tomato hornworm and the Madagascar (hissing) cockroach.

Tomato Hornworm Caterpillars

In nature, tomato hornworm caterpillars feed on the leaves of tomato plants. However, preparing an artificial diet is much easier than growing your own tomato plants. All the nutrients (including water) are present in the artificial diet. The diet is placed in a plastic container with ventilation designed to strike a balance between too much moisture loss from the diet and too much moisture condensation in the container. Placing the diet in a container that is too large will allow the diet to dry and no longer contain enough water.

A plastic container with a clear lid allows for easy observation of the caterpillar. When the caterpillar is small, it is fragile and difficult to handle. When it grows larger than a centimeter in diameter, it can be handled gently without damage. The caterpillar will produce waste (called frass) that should be removed occasionally. If the caterpillar consumes most of the diet, more diet should be added.

Once your caterpillar reaches full size, it will stop eating and begin to wander. It may bite and spit out its food or otherwise mess its food without eating it. At this "wandering" stage, your caterpillar is looking for a place to pupate. In nature, your caterpillar would dig a chamber in the soil to pupate. In your container, you can provide your caterpillar with a tissue paper that it will chew and make a nest. The tissue is less messy than the diet.

Once the pupa has formed, it can be transferred to an emergence cage. A plastic shoe box makes great emergence cage. The pupa can be placed on a paper towel on one end of the box. A stick can be placed in the box to provide a vertical surface for the adult to climb. The box can be stored on end (so the long axis is vertical) on a bookshelf. A clear box will allow you to observe your insect.

The pupa can move, but its movement is restricted. A pupa that is alive will sometimes wriggle when held. The pupa stage typically lasts over 2 weeks. The pupa has a visible extension at one end where the mouthparts will form. Another distinct area of the pupa is the area where the wings will form. Watching an adult emerge from the pupa and spread its wings is fascinating.

The moth will split the cuticle of the pupa case and emerge with its wings folded to fit in the pupa and its cuticle soft and flexible. In order for the wings to fully expand, the moth needs to be in a vertical position. The adult will climb up a stick placed in the container and rest there to expand its wings. Moths expand their wings by forcing fluid into the wing veins. Once emerged, the insect cuticle will harden. If the wings are not properly expanded, they will harden in a shriveled, deformed state that will not allow them to fly. Because hornworms are pests it is best to not release them.

Madagascar Cockroaches

Madagascar cockroaches will do well in any type of terrarium setting. Your cockroach will need a source of water. However, if you give it water in an open container, it will likely make a mess. Water can be provided by sealing a vial of water with a cotton plug. Make sure that the plug stays moist. Water wicks into the cotton and provides sufficient water for the insect without making the rearing arena so moist as to cause microorganisms and fungi to grow. Cockroaches will eat a variety of foods (so experiment!). Do remove uneaten food so it does not rot. Keep the container clean.

Madagascar cockroaches are relatively strong and are capable of pushing lids off weakly sealed containers. It is useful to have a lid that locks in place or to weight the lid with a rock or other heavy object. Roaches are often more active at night than during the day. They may prefer a harborage (a toilet paper roll or cardboard tent works well).

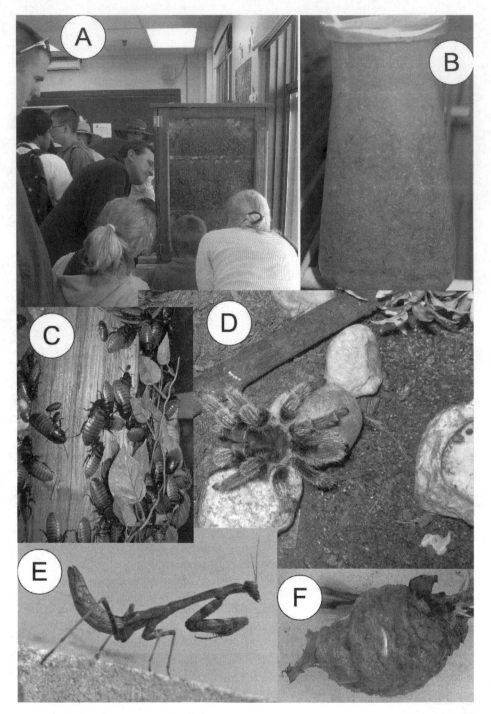

A. An observation hive is used to teach about honey bees. Honey bees are the most commonly reared insect and the most economically important.   B. A flask containing fruit flies. Fruit fly research has made many contributions to science, especially to genetics.   C. Some insects such as the Madagascar hissing cockroach are sold in pet stores and make good pets.   D. Spiders, especially large tarantulas, are kept as pets by spider enthusiasts.   E. Many insects are reared and sold as biological control agents. The praying mantid is popular among home gardeners but other insects are more effective for control of specific pests.   F. Mantids are typically purchased as egg cases. Dozens of praying mantids will hatch from this egg case. They must disperse because they are cannibalistic.

Chapter 14 Study Questions

1. What is the primary motive for rearing the following insects?
   a. Honey bee

   b. Predators and parasitoids

   c. Meal worms

   d. Hissing cockroaches

   e. Dermestid beetles

f. Fruit flies

2. Why is the light-dark cycle important to maintaining insect colonies?

3. Why should people who rear large numbers of insects try to limit their exposure to them?

4. What are the advantages of artificial diets for insects compared to live hosts.

5. What needs to be done for the following life stages of the hornworm caterpillar to rear them successfully?
   a. Larva

   b. Wandering stage larva

c. Pupa

d. Adult

6. Why is the size of the container important in rearing hornworms?

7. What is needed to successfully rear hissing cockroaches?

Chapter 15

Insects as Food

Many cultures throughout the world use insects as part of their diet. In some areas such as the deserts of Australia, Witchetty grubs and other insects were a major source of protein for the Aborigine population. Cultures, such as the Western European cultures, are an exception that do not use insects. However, Western Europeans commonly consume other arthropods, such as marine crustaceans (shrimp, lobster, and crab). In North America, insects are rare in the diets of Canadians and U.S. residents, but are more common in Mexico where caterpillars (gusanos) are served.

The Nutrition of Eating Insects

As discussed in the chapter on insect nutrition, all cells contain the same basic nutrient groups. Cells and tissues differ in the relative abundance of nutrients, the defensive chemicals that are present and secretions of those cells. Within an organism, cells and tissues may differ greatly in the abundance of nutrients. This can give rise to feeding specialization such as insects that feed on fur or cartilage. Compared to plants, the soft tissues of all animals (including those of insects) are more similar are more similar to each other. In general, animals have higher proportions of protein and lower proportion of carbohydrates than plants.

Insects can be a good source of protein and other nutrients, calories and fiber. In some insects, crude protein may reach as high as 60 percent of body content, higher than in common meats such as chicken. Insects such as caterpillars and termites are high in fat and calories per unit weight. Insects store much of their energy as a sugar (trehalose) that can be digested by humans and converted to other sugars as an energy source.

The insect body is enclosed in an exoskeleton consisting of secreted proteins and chitin. Although humans possess chitinases (enzymes that can digest chitin) chitin is poorly digested in the upper digestive tract. Like cellulose, chitin that is non-digestible acts as a fiber. Chitin may be added to some foods to boost fiber content or used as a feed additive. Commercially marketed chitin typically is produced from marine crustaceans rather than insects. This is due to the availability of exoskeleton produced by the processing of shellfish.

What Insects Are Eaten?

The insects used as food vary among cultures and come from many taxonomic groups, including Orthoptera, Hemiptera, Dictyoptera, Isoptera, and larvae of Coleoptera, Lepidoptera, and Hymenoptera. The list of insects used as food exceeds 1,500 species.

Many plants are relatively well defended against feeding by most animals. This precludes the utilization of most plants as sources of food for humans. Animals (including humans) can secondarily use inedible plants to derive nutrition by feeding on animals (including insects) that are capable of eating those plants. For example, some species of insect feed on woody tissues of trees that humans cannot digest. However, the insect larvae can be digested and are used by humans as food. Eating insects as food can expand the sources of nutrition for human populations.

Soft-bodied insects are preferred over adults with hard cuticle. An insect with a hardened exoskeleton is more difficult to process and digest than an unsclerotized larva. Some of the large insects that are eaten, such as grasshoppers, have leg spines that could interfere with swallowing so the legs are removed before consumption. A few insects have spines that can interfere with digestion (such as dermestid beetle larvae) and should not be eaten.

Not all insects are edible. Some insects are toxic and advertise with bright warning colors and a bitter taste. Generally any insect with bright warning coloration should be avoided. Some insects that feed on toxic plants sequester and concentrate the plant toxins in their tissue. For example, monarch butterflies and milkweed bugs that feed on milkweed are known to concentrate cardiac glycosides from the milkweed plant and store them for defense against predators. Both of these insects have bright orange and black warning markings. Mammals that eat these insects may become sick and regurgitate.

Many cultures have substantial knowledge about the edibility of plants and insects that they commonly encounter. Information on edible insects is available in books, including a number of cookbooks that identify edible insects and suggest recipes. Insects may be domesticated and processed for sale in domestic and international markets. Many processed insects are sold at ethnic food stores in the United States or can be ordered for delivery.

Domestication of insects for production and sale as food is a minor industry in some locales. An example is the mopane caterpillar production in Southern Africa. Producers of mopane caterpillars cultivate mopane trees and artificially infest them with mopane caterpillars for harvest. The mopane caterpillars can be sold fresh to local markets or may be dried and processed for storage and export.

Mealworms are larvae of beetles and are commonly marketed in the United States as pet food, although they are edible and suitable for human consumption. There are numerous commercial suppliers of mealworms in the United States. Mealworms can be easily reared on flour supplemented with a protein source such as yeast and adequate humidity. Mealworms can be stir fried as a crispy snack. Mealworms can also be baked and ground to produce flour for use by people with food allergies.

The nutritional value of mealworms can be modified by "gut loading." Practiced by some pet owners, the mealworms are placed on a nutrient rich diet prior to feeding to a pet. The mealworm with the nutrient rich diet "loaded" into its gut is fed to the pet. The pet gets the benefit of the mealworm and its nutritious gut contents.

Those familiar with mezcal or tequila have probably encountered the "worm" in the bottom of the bottle of certain brands. These are not worms. They are caterpillars (gusanos) that feed on the maguey plants used in mescal and tequila production. The presence of the caterpillar advertises that the tequila is made from maguey. Insufficient alcohol concentration would lead to degradation of the gusanos. Well-preserved gusanos indicate a quality product that is produced from maguey and contains sufficient alcohol.

Unintentional Insect Consumption

Consuming insects is unavoidable because insects contaminate many food items. The agency responsible for regulating food and food safety in the United States, the U.S. Food and Drug Administration (FDA), recognizes the impossibility of excluding all insects and insect parts from foods. Instead the FDA regulates the maximum level of insects and insect parts in commercially sold food. Although most insects are not harmful, some such as dermestid beetle larvae can cause gastrointestinal problems because of hooked hairs that lodge in the intestine. However, dermestids are one of the few exceptions. No harm comes from ingestion of most insect parts in food.

The FDA demands that food be prepared under sanitary conditions and excessive insect parts in commercial foods is interpreted as evidence of unsanitary food preparation conditions. The U.S. FDA publishes "Food Action Defect Levels" and will recall food that exceeds those limits. Small amounts of insects and insect parts in food below the FADL are not considered harmful.

The FDA has laboratories that conduct routine inspections of food for insect parts and other adulterations. Many of the contaminating insect parts require a microscope and a trained eye to spot them in the food. Processing causes insects to break into small pieces that may be difficult or impossible to identify. The hard insect head is heavily sclerotized and is the insect part most likely to survive the processing intact and get counted by FDA inspectors. Because of negative perception of insects in food by many Americans, food processors often set standards for insect parts that are well below the standards that are required to meet FDA regulations.

Some of the foods that commonly contain some insect parts are processed fruits and vegetables. Tomatoes attract fruit flies that lay eggs on the fruit, rapidly hatch, and can add tiny larvae to the tomato sauce, paste or ketchup. Mushrooms are home to tiny flies and beetles that live in the mushroom veins under the caps. These are nearly impossible to remove and are not easily noticeable in processed mushrooms.

Occasionally, large insects such as grasshoppers enter processed foods. Large insects are easier for the processor to spot and remove from the product. However, large insects that make it through the processing and into the hands of consumers are also easier for consumers to detect. Large insects in processed food often generate complains, so manufacturers take precautions to eliminate them from the product.

A. Most insect parts in food are small and undetectable as demonstrated in this taste test challenge of food prepared with and without added insect parts. B. Visitors to the Purdue BugBowl can taste recipes made with insects such as mealworm stir-fry. C. Mealworms are commonly used as food for pets because they are easy to rear on inexpensive materials, in this case, oatmeal and yeast. Mealworms are edible by humans. D. The mezcal contains a caterpillar that feeds on maguey. The caterpillar indicates that the distillate comes from maguey and the alcohol content is sufficient

(*continued on page 243*)

Chapter 15 Study Questions

1. How do insects as food compare with meat?

2. In which areas of the world are insects commonly used as food items?

3. In which areas of the world is it uncommon to eat insects?

4. What insects in food are harmful?

(plate caption *continued*)

to preserve the caterpillar.   E. Honey, a sweetener used in all parts of the world, is produced by bees. The bees collect nectar from plants and transport it back to their hive in their crop (part of their digestive system). The nectar is regurgitated and stored in the honey comb.   F. Silkworm pupae are one of the many types of insects that are processed and marketed internationally.   G. It is impossible to avoid consuming some insect parts with food. Insect parts are common in some ground spices.   H. The ingredients of pizza commonly have some insect contamination. Fruit flies lay eggs and larvae hatch in tomatoes before being processed into sauce. Tiny flies can live in the caps of mushrooms, Flour may contain pieces of mealworms or meal moths.

5. Are most insects in food harmful?

6. Is it possible to remove all insects from processed food?

7. What U.S. agency is responsible for setting rules on insect parts in food and inspecting the food?

References

Holmes, Oliver Wendell. 1882. The Poet at the Breakfast- Table. Project Gutenberg 2006-08-15. Accessed August 1, 2008, from http://infomotions.com/etexts/gutenberg/dirs/2/6/6/2666/2666.htm

Norman F. Johnson and Charles A. Triplehorn. 2004. *Borror and DeLong's Introduction to the Study of Insects*, 7th edition. San Francisco: Brooks Cole.

David Grimaldi and Michael S. Engel. 2005. *Evolution of the Insects.* New York: Cambridge University Press.

Timothy J. Gibb and Christian Y. Oseto. 2006. *Collection and Identification of Insects: Field and Laboratory Techniques.* Academic Press.

Michael Dickinson. 2001. *Solving the mystery of Insect Flight.* Scientific American 284: 48–57.

Peter W. Price. 1997. *Insect Ecology*, 3rd Edition. New York: Wiley.

Guy Theraulaz and Eric Bonabeau. 1999. *A brief history of stigmergy.* Artifical Life 5: 97–116.

Defoliart, Gene. 1992. Insects as Human Food. *Crop Protection*, 11:395–399.